WILD ORCHIDS OF DORSET

Martin N. Jenkinson

Cover: Bee Orchid (*Ophrys apifera*) on Fontmell Down.
Frontispiece: Early Spider Orchid (*Ophrys sphegodes*) on a Purbeck limestone meadow.
Back cover: Green-Veined Orchids (*Orchis morio*) on Avon Forest Park.

Publication Data

Copyright — text and all illustrations:
M. N. Jenkinson.

Published in 1991 by
Orchid Sundries Ltd.,
New Gate Farm, Stour Provost,
Gillingham, Dorset, SP8 5LT.

ISBN 1 873 03502 0

Typeset in 11 on 12pt Baskerville

Printed in Great Britain by
Blackmore Press, Shaftesbury, Dorset.

To a good friend,
who helped me find my soul again.

Contents

All line drawings, figures and photographs are by the author.

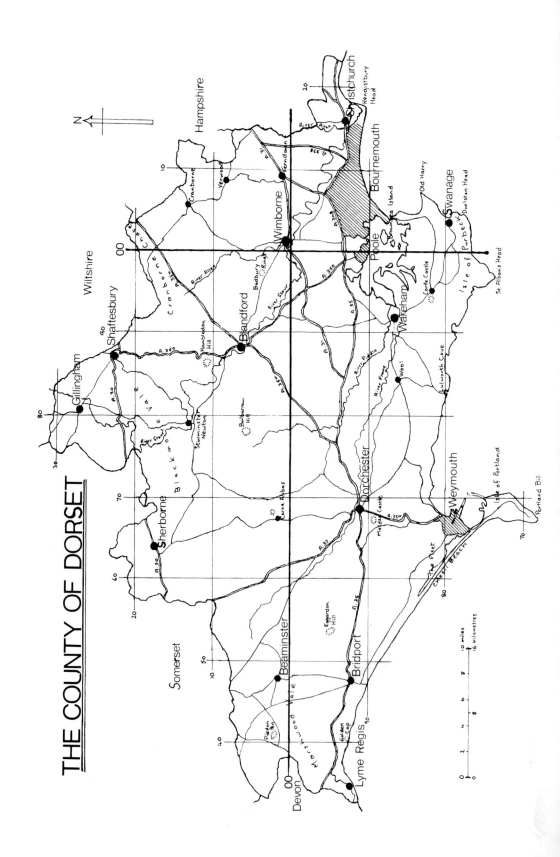

Introduction

In Dorset we are fortunate enough to be living in one of the most picturesque and comparatively unspoilt counties in Britain: hundreds of thousands of holidaymakers testify annually to its attractions, and many of them visit us expressly to savour its natural beauty. There is much in the county to appeal to the specialist naturalist and observant rambler alike: the combination of peace and tranquillity, magnificent unspoilt scenery and an abundance of wildlife is an enviable one.

Our native wild orchids have a peculiar mystique all their own: I fell under their spell over thirty years ago with the chance discovery of a solitary specimen of the strange Bird's Nest Orchid (*Neottia nidus-avis*) in a beechwood in Wimborne St. Giles.

In all there are just under fifty species of orchid which grow wild in the British Isles — a fact which may astonish some people — and many of them are among the greatest rarities of our native flora. Very few indeed can be regarded as anything approaching common. Several are restricted to one or two localities, and may be reduced at those sites to half-a-dozen plants or less. Some locations are known only to small groups of dedicated conservationists and local naturalists, who often mount a twenty-four-hour guard over the plants when they are in flower. Even so, they are still under constant threat from the depredations of herbivores, from adverse ecological and climatic conditions, and from the pressures of rapacious developers and planners attempting to satisfy the all-consuming needs of a highly mobile commercial and residential society for food and lodging. The vast majority of our orchids, even if not in the upper bracket of national rarities, are subjected to increasing pressures on their restricted and specialised habitats, usually as a direct result of man's influence on his environment, and many of them, unless greater public awareness can be fostered, will become endangered in the not too distant future.

The fascination of their real or comparative rarity is only enhanced by their unusual individual qualities: the somewhat bizarre and bewitching beauty of the members of the Bee Orchid family, the mysterious life-cycle of the Bird's Nest Orchid, and the intoxicating perfume of the Fragrant and Butterfly Orchids all conspire to make the magnetism of the group as a whole irresistible.

In Dorset we are exceptionally well-endowed with native wild orchids, a total of thirty-four species being recorded in the county, of which twenty-eight occur regularly, including two, the Early Spider Orchid (*Ophrys sphegodes*) and Lizard Orchid (*Himantoglossum hircinum*), which are listed in the Schedule of endangered and specially protected species in the Wildlife and Countryside Act 1981. Two other scheduled orchids have been reported in the county, although the very old record for the Late Spider Orchid (*Ophrys holoserica*), which now only occurs in Kent, is almost certainly a recording error, and the persistent rumour of Red Helleborine (*Cephalanthera rubra*) in north Dorset woods cannot be confirmed. The record for the Man Orchid (*Aceras anthropophorum*) is old and unconfirmed, the Lesser Twayblade (*Listera cordata*) has not been seen in the county since the turn of the century (although it could still occur), the record for Northern Marsh Orchid (*Dactylorhiza majalis* ssp. *purpurella*) near Dorchester is as yet unconfirmed, and the record for Sword-Leaved Helleborine (*Cephalanthera longifolia*) at Cranborne is almost certainly a recording error. Several other species, such as the Burnt Orchid (*Orchis ustulata*), Musk Orchid (*Herminium monorchis*), Narrow-Leaved Marsh

Orchid (*Dactylorhiza majalis* ssp.*traunsteinerioides*), Slender-Lipped Helleborine (*Epipactis leptochila*), Green-Flowered Helleborine (*Epipactis phyllanthes*) and Violet Helleborine (*Epipactis purpurata*), though nationally not in the 'endangered species' category, are always very local in occurrence, and in Dorset can be considered rarities within the regional context.

There are many locations rich in orchids in the county to which access is restricted in some way, either by virtue of being protected local nature reserves, or where private landowners need to be approached for permission to visit. Such permission is usually forthcoming, however, to the *bona fide* enquirer, and a properly considerate attitude is essential in order to maintain this hard-earned goodwill, particularly of private landowners: any abuse of it will jeopardise not only the facility for others to see great beauty in its natural setting, but may even in the long term threaten the plants themselves. A landowner who voluntarily preserves in its natural state a piece of potentially valuable land for the sake of its flora or fauna, and whose generous hospitality is abused, can hardly be blamed for losing patience and withdrawing the facility from further visitors, and perhaps even for putting the land to what he may see in the short term as a better use. Provision is made in law for measures to be taken to protect threatened sites, but they are rather cumbersome, full of loopholes, and often too slow in effect to achieve the desired objective. It is therefore infinitely preferable where possible to conserve through co-operation and consent — a policy which has been followed to good effect in Dorset.

It is my personal view, however, that the risk of malicious damage to or uprooting of scarce or endangered species is comparatively small in these more enlightened times. There is no excuse for the irresponsible 'collector' who deprives others of the sight and experience of these lovely plants, and incidentally prevents thousands of seeds which might have safeguarded their future from maturing. The sad legacy of the Victorian passion for herbarium or garden 'collections' is a number of rare species which might otherwise have been more readily accessible to us. Fortunately conservation and the environment nowadays are concepts in greater vogue.

That solitary Bird's Nest Orchid at Wimborne St. Giles not only started me on my thirty-year odyssey, but was also my first dreadful mistake: I picked it, suffering from the dilemma of many an amateur naturalist coming upon an unidentified species for the first time, and not having to hand the means to draw or photograph it. Neither is there any malice in the little girl who picks a bunch of flowers for her schoolteacher. Unfortunately, if she happens to live in Purbeck, that bunch could include a few spikes of the Early Spider Orchid, and her sweet innocent gesture in itself could pose a threat to the future survival of the species. In what may be an apocryphal story, it is reported that within living memory, two spikes of that great rarity, the Ghost Orchid (*Epipogium aphyllum*), were picked by schoolchildren in an old beechwood near Shaftesbury, and taken into school in Tollard Royal, where a knowledgeable schoolteacher was able to identify them. It is a thrilling, if sad story — and the species has not been seen since. Whatever the truth may be, the wood concerned (just over the county border in Wiltshire) is an ideal habitat for this rarest of British orchids, and is now in the care of a conservation authority. The species is notoriously erratic in its flowering, and if by some remote chance it were to reappear, it might stand a chance of survival.

On a wider front, the lack of knowledge of the farmer or developer, who may only see his piece of land as a potential source of food or profit, cannot be criticised unless steps are taken towards education into a broader appreciation of the environment: it is my experience that when a landowner is told that he has a rare orchid growing on his land, he is pleased and proud, and only too happy to assist in its protection.

No threat to our precious rarities can afford to be ignored, but the potential risks have to be balanced against each other: the ability to share our heritage through education towards an appreciation of its value is more constructive than a policy of careful concealment. After all, there is little point in concealment against deliberate damage or theft, if it is not practicable to mount round-the-clock security against depredation through accident or ignorance. It is said that the Forestry Commission was not aware of the presence of the Summer Ladies' Tresses (*Spiranthes aestivalis*) on its land in the New Forest when the land was drained after the Second World War: the species is now probably extinct in this country. A positive policy of opening rarity sites to the public on certain days of the year in Kent and Suffolk has paid dividends: thousands of visitors have been able to see the Monkey Orchid (*Orchis simia*), Military Orchid (*Orchis militaris*) and Late Spider Orchid under careful supervision, and have had no detrimental effects on the orchids themselves.

Records Past and Present

No study of any aspect of the flora of Dorset would be complete without due acknowledgement to the great pioneers of Dorset botany. The monumental works of botanists like John Clavell Mansell-Pleydell (Flora of Dorsetshire 1874 and 1895), the Rev. E. F. Linton (Flora of Bournemouth 1900) and Professor Ronald Good (A Geographical Handbook of the Dorset Flora 1948) have made an enormous contribution to our knowledge of the plants of our county, and form the foundation of modern records. In respect of our orchids, however, they suffer from a number of deficiencies. As with many modern Floras, the scope for detailed treatment of the orchids is limited within the bounds of a general flora. Mansell-Pleydell and Linton do not record several species, such as the Lizard Orchid, Burnt Orchid, Musk Orchid and some of the more critical Helleborines, either because they occurred outside the limits of their survey area, had not hitherto been recorded, or were not then recognised as distinct species. Similarly modern research into the Dactylorchids renders many records for members of this group unreliable. Good, whilst more comprehensive in terms of species recorded, misses many sites for our orchids, because the purpose of his work was to establish patterns of distribution rather than to produce an exhaustive account of sites for individual species. I have attempted in this book to fill some of the gaps in our local knowledge: as a specialised treatment of our orchids it is possible, within certain limitations, to be fairly comprehensive.

The distribution maps indicate occurrences of each species within one kilometre squares, following Ordnance Survey National Grid lines, and are based on records held at the Dorset Environmental Records Centre, to whose staff I am indebted, and on my own records. They are certainly therefore more comprehensive than earlier authorities. They are nevertheless perforce incomplete: readers will no doubt know of sites for some species in the unshaded areas of the maps. In addition, many old records for the more critical groups such as the Dactylorchids and Helleborines have had to be disregarded because of taxonomic difficulties: the records I have used for these groups are generally no more than about ten years old. Furthermore, one can only work on the basis of available information: official records can never be complete unless an informed public is able and prepared to notify all sites to the recording authorities. Within each shaded kilometre square there is no indication of the age or comparative density of records, or of the numbers of plants at any site: in the square there may be one record or many, or the species recorded may even by now be extinct. In order to keep faith with the many people who have entrusted me with site information in confidence, I have been unable to be more specific as to precise sites for individual species. It will be possible, however, in most cases, by careful consideration of the maps together with a working knowledge of the preferred habitat of each species, to identify and make enjoyable searches of likely areas, with every chance of being amply rewarded for the effort.

Acknowledgements

Information, access and permission to visit sites has been provided by, amongst many others, the late Monty Banks, Rex Clive, Len Hatchard, Dr. Lesley Haskins, Mark Holloway, Anne Horsfall, Wing Commander Hugh Hunt, Mike Hunt, Richard Laurence, Geoff Marsh, Angela Newton, David Pearman, Lord Shaftesbury and the Shaftesbury Estates, Nigel Trebble, the late Lyn Watson, Jim White, Mrs. M. H. Whitlock, and Felicity Woodhead, and I am grateful for their help.

For initial support, his reading of the first draft, access to his fine collection of orchids and orchid literature, and enthusiastic continued encouragement, I am grateful to Dr. Tom Norman, and for her excellent typing of that crucial first draft, my thanks go to Audrey Pole. For his help with the difficult Helleborines and much valued accompanied fieldwork, I am indebted to R. Paul Bowman. For her loan of reference works, encouragement and helpful fieldwork, I thank Felicity Woodhead.

For much valued help with the Dactylorchids, and their exhaustive but constructive criticism of the final manuscript, I acknowledge my considerable debt to Dr. Richard Bateman and Dr. Ian Denholm. There are others, too numerous to mention, who have helped along the way: they know who they are, and I thank them as well. Finally, I thank Norman Heywood for his enthusiasm, encouragement and commitment, without which this book would probably not have been published.

Objectives

This book is aimed principally at the unconverted, but I have tried also to present helpful and up-to-date information which is of interest to the more knowledgeable botanist, particularly in areas subject to recent and continuing research, such as the Helleborines and Dactylorchids. My classifications broadly follow Flora Europaea Vol. 5, (Tutin et al 1980) with the exceptions of *Epipactis phyllanthes* (where I follow the late Dr. D. P. Young (1952 and 1962)) and the Dactylorchids, in which I am myself closely involved in current research, and in which I follow R. M. Bateman and I. Denholm (1983, 85 and 89).

I have set out in particular to fill what I see as two major gaps in orchid literature. Firstly, I have attempted to combine in one volume an account, albeit sketchy, of the relationship between geology, soils and habitat, and their associated orchid flora. An idea of the extent to which these various aspects are divorced from each other in botanical literature will be gained from an examination of the research references which I have had to use just to produce the brief account in this book. Secondly, most botanical reference books, with a few significant exceptions, make heavy weather of the identification of critical species by means of dry textual scientific descriptions or the ubiquitous flower 'keys'. There seems to me to be no substitute for good quality colour photographs, including full plant shots to show leaf formation and markings, overall appearance and something of habitat, and close-up shots to reveal the fine detail of floral structure, colour and markings that so often contribute to an accurate identification. The colour plates are prepared from transparencies all of which I have taken myself, mostly in Dorset — the few exceptions are clearly identified.

Working on the assumption that public awareness and concern are vital to the continued survival of some of our rarest and most beautiful plants, I have attempted in this book to enable those with little or no knowledge of our native orchids to identify them accurately, and thus come to a greater appreciation of their worth. An increase in accurate recording and notification of species to the conservation and recording authorities would be an invaluable by-product of such increased knowledge.

We have a rich heritage in Dorset: it is our duty to bring it to as wide a respectful public as possible, and to foster a sense of caring collective responsibility and sharing in community wealth.

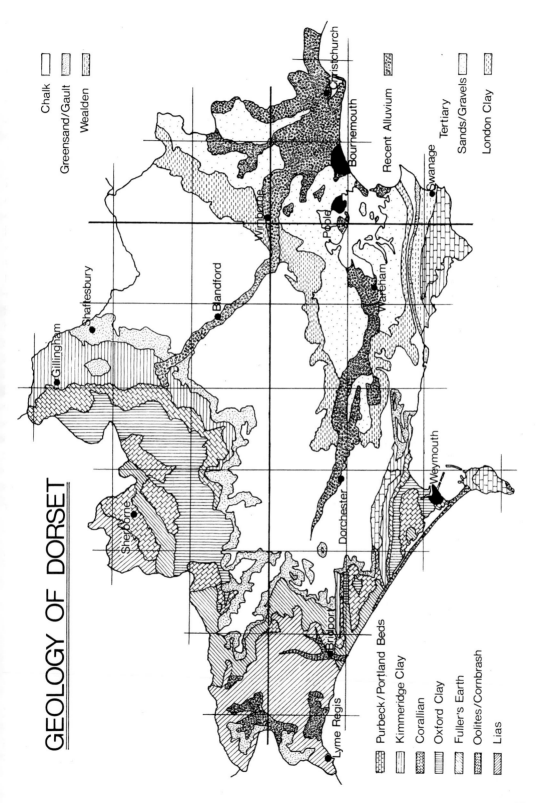

GEOLOGY OF DORSET

Chalk

Greensand/Gault

Wealden

Recent Alluvium

Tertiary

Sands/Gravels

London Clay

Purbeck/Portland Beds

Kimmeridge Clay

Corallian

Oxford Clay

Fuller's Earth

Oolites/Cornbrash

Lias

Gillingham

Shaftesbury

Blandford

Sherborne

Wimborne

Christchurch

Bournemouth

Poole

Swanage

Wareham

Dorchester

Weymouth

Bridport

Lyme Regis

The Geology of Dorset

I have found over the years that some knowledge of the geology of an area has been a help to me in my search for orchids. The relationship between geology, soils and vegetation is a complex one, and to deal with it in detail is beyond the scope of this book. Nevertheless, orchids in many cases have specific and limited habitat requirements, and it may be found helpful to have some understanding of the conditions leading to the occurrence of those habitats.

Although there are no really old rocks in Dorset, in terms of the vast geological time-scale, the cross-section of rock formations to be found is quite remarkable for such a small area. It can best be visualised as a series of large concentric half-circles or horseshoes, with the open end facing east towards Hampshire, dominated by the broad belt of chalk entering the county in the north-east through Cranborne Chase, heading south-west and broadening into central Dorset, and then swinging back east and petering out in the Isle of Purbeck. The older rocks lie on the outer rim of this broad half-circle, to the west, and the more recent deposits lie inside the arms of the horseshoe of chalk and to the east of it.

The oldest rocks in Dorset are about 210 million years old, and are from the Jurassic period, the age of the dinosaurs, and consist of a complex series of limestones, marls, shales, clays and sandstones, all more or less calcareous. The Lias is prominent in the west of the county around Lyme Regis, forming the characteristic coastal formations of tumbling clay landslips with alternating layers of limestone, such as those at Black Ven and Spittles. Calcareous drainage water filtering through the limestone layers is often trapped in the blue clay layers, forming marshes which support a rich flora, including several orchid species. Upper layers of the Lias include some calcareous sandstone deposits such as those of Golden Cap and Thorncombe Beacon, and where sandstones predominate some local surface leaching of minerals through the porous sandstone may occur, creating local pockets of acid soil.

The Oolites and Cornbrash form a broad belt of limestones, clays, sands, marls and flagstones meandering in an intermittent band from Chickerell, Abbotsbury and the Fleet in the south, along the coast to Burton Bradstock, northwards through Bridport, Bothenhampton, Chideock Quarry Hill and Beaminster towards Crewkerne and Corscombe, and then reappearing in a broad belt from Yetminster towards Milborne Port south and east of Sherborne. These formations are characterised by a prominent ridge of higher ground of porous limestone resting on the Forest Marble clays and limestones of the Upper Oolite, creating local springs along the line of the outcrop.

The Jurassic clays (the Oxford and Kimmeridge beds) consist of greenish or blue-grey clays, with some sandy beds, muddy marine sediments with nodules of calcareous mudstone and some hard stone bands, and are separated by a narrow belt of Corallian limestone. The Oxford Clay forms Blackmore Vale and other characteristic wolds between the ridges formed by the older Jurassic limestones and the Corallian beds, and the Kimmeridge Clay is well displayed at the Hounstout cliffs of Chapmans Pool, Kimmeridge Bay, Ringstead Bay Osmington and Abbotsbury. In places there are layers of bituminous clays which can burn spontaneously, and many of the shales of the Kimmeridge Clay are also oil-bearing. Clay deposits form typical flat tracts of land between the ridges of the harder limestones, which are slower to weather. The Kimmeridge Clay reappears in a broad belt north of the chalk, from

Sturminster Newton out of the northern spur of the county between Gillingham and Shaftesbury. The Corallian limestone forms the ridge from Mappowder northwards through Sturminster Newton between the Kimmeridge Clay and the Oxford Clay of Blackmore Vale.

The most recent Jurassic formations are the massive limestones of the Isles of Portland and Purbeck which support extensive areas of limestone grassland of national importance for their flora and butterflies, and a thriving quarry industry based on the fine building qualities of their famous stones.

Early Cretaceous clays and sands known as the Wealden Beds form the gentle wolds between the limestone ridges and the chalk, such as those at Swanage, Worbarrow, Mupe Bay and Lulworth Cove, and which run from Gillingham to the Vale of Wardour in the north of the county.

The later sands, clays, sandstones and grits of the Greensand and Gault form a narrow belt across Dorset from south-west to north-east between the Wealden Beds and the chalk. From Abbotsbury they run north-west to Mosterton, and then swing north-east to the Vale of Wardour and Shaftesbury. Light greenish or blue-grey sands and sandstones give way to the bluish-grey clays of the Gault. These deposits become progressively sandier towards the west of the county, as in outcrops at Pilsdon Pen, Lewesdon Hill, Hardon Hill, and the caps of Black Ven, Stonebarrow and Golden Cap.

However, it is above all else the chalk that forms the dominant physiological features of the Dorset landscape: the gentle rolling hills of the central massif of the Dorset Downs, of Cranborne Chase, and of the sinuous belt across Purbeck which forms the secondary ridge through Corfe Castle, ending in the dramatic rocks of Old Harry. This is where the chalk ridge was breached by the Eocene sea, and the same ridge reappears at the Needles and forms the backbone of the Isle of Wight. The short downland turf of shallow rendzina soils, and the rich woodlands of the deeper soils of recent superficial deposits over the chalk alike are a botanist's paradise, and support many of the rarer species of the Dorset flora, including many orchids.

East of and inside the broad horseshoe of the chalk, early Eocene deposits form a narrow belt of London Clay, which consists mainly of wet heavy soils which are particularly prone to trapping the drainage water from the chalk in marshy hollows which support a rich fenland flora.

Later Eocene and Pleistocene deposits form the broad basin centred on Poole and Bournemouth, and extend eastwards into the Hampshire Basin: these are acid sands, clays and gravels which support the floristically important areas of heathland, bog, open coniferous woodland and ancient oak and beech forests of east Dorset and the New Forest.

The range of geological formations in Dorset is quite remarkable for such a comparatively small area, and contributes in no small measure to the rich variety of plant communities which flourish on its soils.

Orchid Habitats

The essential complement to the analysis of the geology of Dorset in the preceding section is an outline of the various types of plant community which have developed on, and are dependent upon those rocks and their associated soils: the two subjects are inextricably inter-related. An account of the orchids typically to be found in those different ecological environments may then lead to a better understanding of the apparently curious and sporadic distribution of our native wild orchids.

A detailed analysis of plant communities is far beyond the scope of this book, and there are indeed many excellent books dealing in detail with the subject. For our present purposes, however, the main habitats of our native orchids can be classified conveniently as follows:

    A)   Heathland and Moorland,
    B)   Acid Wetland,
    C)   Neutral and Calcareous Wetland,
    D)   Neutral and Calcareous Grassland, and
    E)   Woodland.

These subdivisions are sufficient for broadly helpful groupings of the orchids in terms of ecological requirements, and will be utilised again in the detailed sections on each individual species.

A) *Heathland and Moorland.*

Heathland develops on dry acid soils with little peat overlay, and often on bare sand or gravel: a typical soil is the thin grey sandy soil of our lowland heaths known as podzol. The vegetation is dominated, as might be expected, by various species of heather. Moorland is wetter, allowing a greater depth of peat to develop, and supports a wider variety of plant species, such as coarse grasses, sedges, cotton grasses and purple moor grass, in addition to the heather species. The dividing line, however, is fine, and often difficult to determine. Ling, bell heather, gorse, broom, and the typical acid-soil indicators such as Heath Bedstraw (*Galium saxatile*) and Tormentil (*Potentilla erecta*) are characteristic constituents of such plant communities, and in Dorset the rare Dorset Heath (*Erica ciliaris*) occurs in local abundance on heathland in the Poole Basin.

Orchids usually prefer neutral or calcareous soils: there are, however, a few exceptions, some of which are only found on acid soils. The Heath Spotted Orchid (*Dactylorhiza maculata*) is the most frequently encountered orchid of Dorset heathland, and is characteristic of this habitat, even growing occasionally in the driest, most arid and inhospitable soils, although it is more often found and tends to flourish better in damp peaty hollows. Another species frequently recorded from heathland areas is the Autumn Ladies' Tresses (*Spiranthes spiralis*), although it is usually in the grassy, less acid patches which occur frequently as small fertile oases across the heaths of the Poole Basin and the western fringes of the New Forest. Far less frequently found is the Lesser Butterfly Orchid (*Platanthera bifolia*), an extremely local species found occasionally around the damp fringes of acid bogs on the heathland south of Poole Harbour and elsewhere, but rather more frequently in the New Forest, where it may be found nestling secretively under the protective fronds of bracken along the borders of woods adjacent to areas of heathland. The Greater Twayblade (*Listera ovata*) is common throughout the area, being tolerant of all soil types. Although it is most abundant on chalk downland, it is an occasional constituent of the heathland flora. Its smaller cousin, however, the Lesser Twayblade (*Listera cordata*), is a rare orchid. Typically a species of northern moors and ancient Caledonian pine forests, it was recorded from the Bournemouth area in the late nineteenth century (Linton 1900), and has not been seen in Dorset since. It has been seen more recently in the New Forest, however (1930-33 and possibly as late as the 1970s, although a 1980 record proved to be planted): it is such a small and inconspicuous species that it may conceivably still survive in Hampshire and Dorset. Another rare orchid more frequently encountered in Scotland is the Bog Orchid (*Hammarbya paludosa*), which occurs very locally in a few of the bogs of the heathlands across the Poole Basin, but that is strictly a species of acid wetland (see section B below). Less restricted are the orchids of the sporadic damp peaty hollows that occur across most tracts of heathland, such as the Fragrant Orchid (*Gymnadenia conopsea*) in one or more of its related forms, the Early Marsh Orchid (*Dactylorhiza incarnata*), particularly its deep purple-coloured form, ssp.*pulchella*, and in the less acid patches, the Southern Marsh Orchid (*Dactylorhiza majalis* ssp. *praetermissa*) and Common Spotted Orchid (*Dactylorhiza fuchsii*).

While most of Dorset's heathland has developed on the Tertiary sands and gravels of the Poole Basin, extending westwards to Winfrith Heath, occasional patches of heathland also occur on some sandier deposits of the more westerly Lias and Greensand beds, where leaching by rainfall in exposed sites has washed the free calcium carbonate and other nutrients of normally calcareous soils down into lower levels, creating local pockets of acid soil supporting a heathland flora. Plateau Gravel, a Pleistocene superficial deposit over chalk, can also support a heathland community where leaching has occurred: it can be something of a culture shock to find heather and bracken with Heath Spotted and Lesser Butterfly Orchids growing on the top of chalk downs such as Batcombe Hill in north-west Dorset, and at one or two other places.

Enormous areas of former heathland in the Poole and Hampshire Basins have been lost to forestry, building development and the Ministry of Defence: fortunately much of the precious remainder is subject of various conservation orders, seeking to protect rarities such as the Dorset Heath (*Erica ciliaris*), Marsh Gentian (*Gentiana pneumonanthe*), Sand Lizard, Smooth Snake and Dartford Warbler. No less important are the scarce orchids of this very specialised and declining habitat: no effort must be spared to prevent further losses, and the recent ministerial reprieve of a section of Canford Heath under threat from development was a welcome reversal of the trend of recent years.

B) *Acid Wetland.*

In local depressions on acid sandy soils, where the water table is at or slightly above the surface, either through poor local drainage or by virtue of the general low level of the ground, sphagnum mosses may grow and create a living environment peculiarly their own: the sphagnum bog.

The living mosses absorb nutrients from the water supply, be that rain or ground-water, and release hydrogen ions, making the water more acid. They also absorb water like a sponge and grow upwards, thus raising the water table. As the sphagnum blanket rises it dies away underneath, but does not decompose because of the lack of oxygen. It then forms a growing layer of organic peat which rises steadily as long as the mosses remain healthy. The consequent raising of the water table can often cause a sphagnum bog to spread slowly into surrounding heathland. Its continued growth and lateral spread will only be halted by man's interference through drainage or other alteration, or by climatic variation such as the exceptionally hot dry summers of 1976 and 1984 and more recently in 1989/90, when water may evaporate out of the peripheral areas of sphagnum, which then dies.

Sphagnum bogs generally occur in this area only on patches of locally poor drainage on the naturally acid Tertiary sands and gravels of the Poole Basin, although rarely small pockets of sphagnum moss may develop on peat fens, when the delicate fenland balance has been upset in some way, such as by a drop in the level of calcareous drainage water. In the broader national context climatic factors, such as consistently high rainfall in western Ireland, north Wales and Scotland, may contribute to the formation of blanket bogs. Locally the lowering of the general water table, through increasing extraction for domestic and agricultural purposes, may upset the pH levels of valley marshes.

A very specialised plant community thrives in the highly acidic conditions of the sphagnum bog. Typical species are the cotton-grasses (*Eriophorum* spp.), the attractive yellow spikes of Bog Asphodel (*Narthecium ossifragum*), the curious rosettes of the insectivorous Sundews (*Drosera* spp.), and the minute furled leaves and pale mauve flowers of the rather local insectivorous Pale Butterwort (*Pinguicula lusitanica*): in the nutrient-poor environment of the acid bog, such species supplement their intake of nutrients with a diet of insects trapped by the sticky leaves. Shrubby herbs such as Bog Myrtle (*Myrica gale*) and various heathers will also flourish in and around the fringes of sphagnum bogs. Clumps of purple moor-grass (*Molinia caerulea*) will often form safe stepping-stones across the more treacherous areas.

Orchid species occurring in true acid bogs are very limited: the tiny Bog Orchid (*Hammarbya paludosa*) is the only species restricted to the wettest and most acid bogs. The Lesser Twayblade (*Listera cordata*) in many of its northern stations grows in sphagnum cushions between the stems of mature heather plants, and could conceivably occur in similar places in our area, as such a specialised habitat makes it extremely difficult to find. The Heath Spotted Orchid (*Dactylorhiza maculata*) occurs regularly around the fringes of bogs, although it tends to avoid the wettest and most acid areas of sphagnum. The dark form of the Early Marsh Orchid (*Dactylorhiza incarnata* ssp. *pulchella*) on the other hand will often be found in the wettest areas. The Lesser Butterfly Orchid (*Platanthera bifolia*) is a much rarer constituent of the flora of the bog fringes.

Where other orchid species, such as the Southern Marsh Orchid (*Dactylorhiza majalis* ssp.*praetermissa*), Marsh Helleborine (*Epipactis palustris*), Marsh Fragrant Orchid (*Gymnadenia conopsea* ssp.*densiflora*), Greater Twayblade (*Listera ovata*) or Common Spotted Orchid (*Dactylorhiza fuchsii*) occur in close proximity to sphagnum bogs, as they often do, it will be found that the extreme acidity of the sphagnum has been neutralised by some external influence, such as a source of calcareous drainage water. A good example of this is on the heathland south of Poole Harbour, where in a number of places the imported chalk rubble used as a foundation for the roads creates artificially calcareous verges, a botanically rich habitat often immediately adjacent to species-poor acid heathland and deep acid bog, and Marsh Helleborine and Bog Orchid can be found a matter of feet apart.

C) *Neutral and Calcareous Wetland.*
Apart from sphagnum bog, and at the other extreme, highly calcareous true fen, the dividing lines between different types of wetland are often blurred and indistinct, sometimes merging and changing from one type to another within a very small area.

The term 'marshland' covers a multitude of different habitat types, ranging from the mildly acid wet peat surrounding areas of sphagnum bog, through a range of muddy hollows on heathland, damp meadow, and shale cliff landslips, to the extensive tracts of calcareous mud, ooze and reedbeds adjoining rivers, covering the full range of pH values. All types have their own characteristic flora, though the boundaries between closely related types may be difficult to determine. For the purposes of this account estuarine saltmarsh can be ignored, as orchids cannot survive in saline conditions.

True 'fens' are wetlands formed on a peat base in which the drainage water or ground water is neutral or alkaline — more often than not, in fact, quite markedly calcareous, such as that for example from springs rising from chalk or limestone into adjacent clay substrates. The peat is bonded by the roots of the lush vegetation, maintaining its level: if the peat rises locally above the calcareous water table, it may become acid and develop a growth of sphagnum (see Acid Wetland (B) above). Fen is rich in nutrients and highly fertile: by its very nature it is also highly unstable, and if not regularly cut or grazed, birch, alder or willow scrub can rapidly invade it, resulting eventually in carr and woodland.

Fenland is also one of the most congenial environments for orchids, and a number of rare species which do not occur in this area are restricted nationally to small pockets of fast disappearing fen. Other orchids, typical of the fenland flora though not restricted to it, which do occur in our area, are the Early Marsh Orchid (*Dactylorhiza incarnata* ssp. *incarnata*), the Southern Marsh Orchid (*Dactylorhiza majalis* ssp.*praetermissa*), the Narrow-Leaved Marsh Orchid (*Dactylorhiza majalis* ssp. *traunsteinerioides*), the Marsh Fragrant Orchid (*Gymnadenia conopsea* ssp.*densiflora*), and the Marsh Helleborine (*Epipactis palustris*). Although the rare Narrow-Leaved Marsh Orchid does not occur in its typical form in Dorset, a recently named variety does occur at one site (albeit not a fenland site) and there are several mixed marsh orchid colonies in the area which contain plants intermediate in form between the Southern and Narrow-Leaved Marsh Orchids. The lovely Marsh Helleborine is locally abundant in several Dorset localities.

True fenland is scarce in Dorset, restricted to a few small pockets in the valleys of rivers draining off the chalk, particularly where the chalk streams run out to the sea across peat moorland over the Tertiary clays. Neutral and calcareous marshland, however, is well represented in the county, with extensive areas of marshland associated with the old water-meadow systems on the alluvium of the valleys of the Rivers Avon, Stour, Frome, Allen and others. All country folk will also know of their own local pockets of damp ground in the corners of their fields and meadows, where low-lying clay hollows hold rainwater, or are regularly inundated by the winter spates of the chalk streams, or where springs from the chalk cause wet flushes in the soils of the London and Oxford Clays on either side of the chalk ridges. A feature of the Lias and Kimmeridge Clay of much of our coastal cliff systems is the formation of small patches of calcareous marsh in the hollows of soft shale landslips, such as those at St. Albans Head, Chapmans Pool, Ringstead Bay, Black Ven and Spittles, which are a rich source of marsh orchid colonies, and often support fine stands of the Marsh Helleborine. Further inland, the surface calcareous gleys characteristic of depressions in the Lias, Gault Clay and Wealden Beds often form local valley marshes, such as those at Powerstock Common, Loscombe and Kilwood nature reserves, which also support fine marsh orchid populations. Many plant species are common to fen, calcareous and neutral marshland, and short of close examination of soil types, and soil testing, it is often difficult to distinguish one from the other. The presence however of a significant peat layer in association with this type of rich plant community is usually an indication of true fen. Some orchid species are tolerant of many different soil types: both Common and Heath Spotted Orchids often occur in quite damp soils, and rarely even occur together, although the Heath Spotted Orchid avoids markedly calcareous soils, and is thus a good neutral marsh indicator. Likewise the Greater Twayblade occurs in all such wetlands almost as regularly as it appears on downland. The Northern

Marsh Orchid (*Dactylorhiza majalis* ssp.*purpurella*) used to occur in a dense neutral marsh in two adjacent localities in Hampshire in addition to its wider northern range, and has been recorded (as yet unconfirmed) in one Dorset locality.

D) *Neutral and Calcareous Grassland.*

Grassland, like fen, is an unstable environment, because it is not a 'climax' plant community in terms of the natural succession of species, and if it is not maintained, dominant shrub and tree species will eventually succeed, and the grassland will be invaded by scrub and woodland.

The thin grey soil of the chalk and limestone hills which supports most of the best of our grassland may not be deep enough to maintain a significant growth of trees, but a scrub cover of brambles, blackthorn, hawthorn, dogwood and wayfaring tree will rapidly develop if it is not controlled. In many places in Dorset, however, the bedrock is overlaid with deeper drift deposits such as Plateau Gravel, Clay-with-Flints, Brickearth or Coombe Deposit, all of which will readily support the growth of trees such as beech, ash, elm, oak or sycamore unless the natural succession is somehow interrupted.

It has been the interference with nature by man that has caused our precious chalk downland and limestone grassland to develop in its present form, with a short herb-rich sward. From prehistoric times it has been the grazing of domestic animals, particularly sheep, with the support of the wild rabbit population, that has created and maintained a close-cropped springy turf particularly suitable, because of the absence of competition, for slow-growing small flowering plants, herbs and fine grasses, and an abundance of orchids including many of our rarest species. Heavy grazing by cattle or the totally destructive grazing of goats (which has destroyed so many Mediterranean orchid sites) or other equally drastic interference such as the use of any form of fertilizer, will upset the delicate downland balance, either by destroying delicate root-systems, or by encouraging the growth of more robust species which will dominate and inhibit the smaller herbs. Equally deleterious, total abandonment of downland by man allows it to revert to scrub and woodland. A careful conservation policy is therefore necessary in order to maintain our precious downland at its magnificent best, and the ancient cause of the evolution of downland is the best means of perpetuating it.

Nationally, calcareous grassland supports more orchids than any other habitat: Bee Orchid (*Ophrys apifera*), Early Spider Orchid (*Ophrys sphegodes*), Green-Veined Orchid (*Orchis morio*), Burnt Orchid (*Orchis ustulata*), Musk Orchid (*Herminium monorchis*), Frog Orchid (*Coeloglossum viride*) and Autumn Ladies' Tresses (*Spiranthes spiralis*) are all species of the shortest turf, and occur in Dorset. Great rarities such as the Monkey Orchid (*Orchis simia*) and Late Spider Orchid (*Ophrys holoserica*) are also found in similar sites in Kent and elsewhere.

Long grassland on chalk and limestone tends to occur on shallower slopes on deeper soil, which will rapidly become overgrown with scrub if allowed to develop unhindered. Pyramidal Orchid (*Anacamptis pyramidalis*) and Man Orchid (*Aceras anthropophorum*) are typical species of such areas, and a number of other orchids, more tolerant of a wide range of conditions, may be found in long and short grass alike, and even in scrub and wood borders: Common Spotted Orchid, Greater Twayblade, Greater Butterfly Orchid, Lesser Butterfly Orchid, Early Purple Orchid (*Orchis mascula*), Fly Orchid (*Ophrys insectifera*), and Fragrant Orchid all occur locally in a wide range of conditions. The very rare Lizard Orchid (*Himantoglossum hircinum*), most often found in chalk scrub, has also recently reappeared in Dorset, and one of the great national rarities, the Military Orchid (*Orchis militaris*), is also found in chalk scrub in Buckinghamshire and Suffolk.

The list of orchids of calcareous grassland is therefore long and impressive: the national decline of such habitat is a cause for considerable concern. Ancient undisturbed calcareous grassland is now a scarce habitat nationally although it is well represented on Dorset reserves. Some of the best sites are on Iron Age hill-forts, or in old chalk diggings and long disused limestone quarries, where the variation of aspect and absence of competition from faster-growing species provides conditions conducive to many species, often within a very small area.

No account of grassland would be complete without reference to that other remarkable creation of human management: the water meadow. Mostly on deeper alluvial soils in river valleys, herb-rich neutral meadows are the product of an economic use of otherwise comparatively uneconomic land. By means of a complex system of flooding and drainage ditches, coupled with river sluices, 17th and 18th century agricultural engineers effectively converted unproductive wet riverside pastures to produce a summer hay harvest and rich autumn and winter grazing for livestock. The grasses, and quite incidentally, the meadow flowers as well, were allowed to set seed before the hay was cut, in order to provide the following year's crop, and regular subsequent grazing maintained a low level of competition from fast-growing species. The by-product of the system was the abundance of meadow flowers such as clover (*Trifolium pratense*), meadow-sweet (*Spiraea ulmaria*), ragged robin (*Lychnis flos-cuculi*) and cuckoo-flower (*Cardamine pratensis*), and a specialised environment conducive to orchids such as the Green-Veined Orchid (*Orchis morio*), sometimes in spectacular abundance, Autumn Ladies' Tresses (*Spiranthes spiralis*), Greater Butterfly Orchid (*Platanthera chlorantha*), Greater Twayblade (*Listera ovata*), and in the damper areas, Southern Marsh and Early Marsh Orchids (*Dactylorhiza* spp.).

Modern farming practices have destroyed the majority of our old hay-meadows, and the decline in the meadow species has paralleled the wholesale destruction of this very specialised habitat, to be replaced by the monotonous monoculture of fast growing grasses for silage. Some meadows are left in Dorset: the valleys of the Avon, Stour, Frome, Allen and Piddle support a few precious remnants of herb-rich meadow, although few of them are managed in the traditional manner. Urgent work is necessary to ensure that no more are destroyed: once lost, they are irretrievable. It is not only nationally rare species such as the Green-Veined Orchid and Snake's Head Fritillary (*Fritillaria meleagris*) that are in jeopardy: if we are not careful, the simple aesthetic beauty of meadows in May and June will be lost to future generations. We often do not miss such things until it is too late, after they have disappeared for good.

E) *Woodland.*

    a)   Coniferous Woodland:

The most important example of coniferous woodland, in terms of botanical interest, is ancient pine forest, which is restricted in the British Isles to the Scottish Highlands, where the last vestiges of the ancient open upland pine forests, that once covered much of what is now moorland and monoculture alien conifer plantations, support such localised rarities as the Lesser Twayblade, Common Coralroot (*Corallorhiza trifida*) and Creeping Ladies' Tresses (*Goodyera repens*). There is no comparable habitat-type in Dorset. The nearest equivalent is small localised pockets of woodland on the western borders of the New Forest, where Scots pine seedlings have established themselves and matured on old heathland. Most such trees have originated from Forestry Commission plantations, and are less than a hundred years old. Generally a heathland flora is maintained, with such orchids as the Heath Spotted Orchid, more rarely in the less acid spots the Common Spotted Orchid, the Greater Twayblade and the scarce Lesser Butterfly Orchid. Southern Marsh and Early Marsh Orchids may flourish in the wetter areas. None of these is a truly woodland species, although the Common Spotted Orchid is frequent in mixed deciduous woodlands on the chalk. The occasional occurrence of the Broad-Leaved or Green-Flowered Helleborines (*Epipactis* spp.) near or amongst pines, as at one or two locations near Hurn in the east of the county, may be evidence of the former existence of older oak woodland long since felled for timber, and replanted with conifers or naturally reseeded with accidental pine invasion.

Modern coniferous plantations are usually too recent in origin or too closely sown to support an orchid flora, unless vestiges of heathland or older woodland floras survive in the more open rides. It may be that in time, where plantations are thinned out and allowed to mature, an orchid flora will develop. Similarly, it may be that in centuries to come, a climax pine forest will develop from the casual seedlings of the New Forest, maturing into a habitat comparable to the ancient Caledonian forests, although the southern climate will militate against a duplication of their sub-arctic/alpine flora.

b)   Deciduous Woodland:

Deciduous or broad-leaved woodland is a much more congenial habitat for orchids, depending on a number of factors, the more important of which are age, dominant canopy species, soil and bedrock, and management. Most woodland in Dorset is mixed deciduous, with some oak, beech and ash, an admixture of sycamore and sweet chestnut, and an understorey of lower-growing species such as rowan, holly and rhododendron. There are comparatively few pure stands of any single species, and very little truly ancient woodland, which is defined as having an unbroken history of woodland on the site for a continuous period of more than three hundred years. It is therefore largely a question of categorising woodland in our area by the soil and bedrock in which they grow, dominant canopy species, comparative age, and type of management.

The best woods for orchids are generally those on calcareous soils in which the dominant canopy species are beech or oak of a reasonable level of maturity (generally 50 years or more), with an open, uncluttered ground flora. A dense understorey militates against a good ground flora. Woods where a traditional 'coppice-with-standards' management regime has been maintained for a long period are also fine hunting grounds for orchids. The regular cyclic cutting of hazel thickets, combined with the maintenance of a proportion of oak or ash standards, provides an ideal environment for many species. The ancient practice of coppicing hazels, by cutting them for thin poles and lathes for woven fencing panels or hurdles, in rotation on a cycle of between seven and fifteen years, and maintaining an open canopy of mature pole-ash and oak standards, is a peculiarly beneficial system for orchids, as it artificially creates conditions suitable for the continued survival of most of the woodland species. A dramatic display of Early Purple and Greater Butterfly Orchids will often follow a cutting of the hazels, as the increased light produces ideal flowering conditions, and the increasingly deep shade of the maturing hazels will provide favourable conditions for the Helleborines (*Epipactis* spp.) and the Bird's Nest Orchid (*Neottia nidus-avis*).

The truly woodland orchids such as the Broad-Leaved, Slender-Lipped, Green-Flowered, Violet and Large White Helleborines, and the saprophytic Bird's Nest Orchid all flourish in various different types of deciduous woodland in Dorset, together with other shade-tolerant species such as the Early Purple Orchid, Greater Butterfly Orchid, Greater Twayblade, Fly Orchid and Common Spotted Orchid. More specific and detailed habitat requirements for individual orchid species will be found in the descriptive sections on each species.

The five broad habitat-types outlined in this chapter are well represented in Dorset's nature reserves, many of which have unrestricted public access, and which are havens for many of our orchid species. The fact that they are easily accessible, however, does not mean that we should not treat them with respect and consideration: the continued survival of many of our rarest species depends to a large extent on the responsible attitude of a caring public.

Follow the Country Code, and do not pick flowers or disturb birds or animals. Close all gates and (where permitted at all) keep your dog on a lead. Do not drop litter or light fires, and comply with the special laws regarding rarities. A special note to photographers: be careful not to trample other plants while you photograph your special rarity!

Dorset's Nature Reserves.

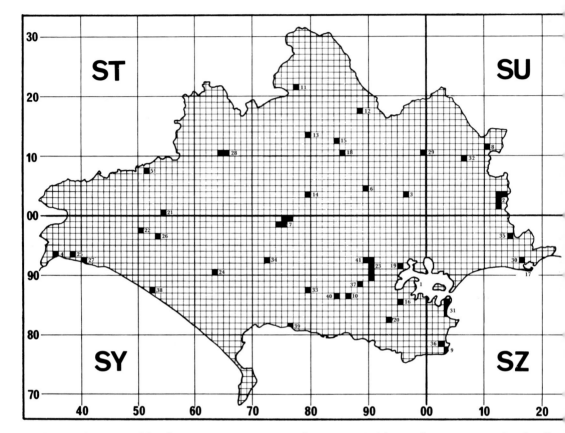

Dorset has a wealth of nature reserves, owned or managed by various conservation bodies aimed at protecting different aspects of our wildlife heritage. Not all of them support orchid populations. The following is a list of those reserves which contain significant orchid colonies their approximate locations being shown on the above map. The letter 'P' indicates that access is restricted to permit-holders only: permits are obtainable from the management bodies for the individual reserves.

Key:

1. Arne (RSPB)
2. Avon Forest Park (DCC)
3. Badbury Rings (NT)
4. Black Ven & Spittles (DTNC)
5. Bracketts Copse (DTNC)
6. Charlton Beeches (WT)
7. Cheselbourne Downs (DTNC)(P)
8. Cranborne Common (DTNC)
9. Durlston Country Park (DCC)
10. East Stoke Fen (DTNC) (P)
11. Fifehead Wood (WT)
12. Fontmell Down (NT & DTNC)(P)
13. Girdler's Coppice (DTNC)(P)
14. Green Hill Down (DTNC)
15. Hambledon Hill (NT & DTNC)(P)
16. Hartland Moor (NT & NCC)(P)
17. Hengistbury Head (BBC)

18. Hod Hill (DTNC)
19. Holton Heath (NCC)(P)
20. Kilwood (DTNC)(P)
21. Kingcombe (DTNC)
22. Loscombe (DTNC)(P)
23. Morden Bog (NCC)(P)
24. Muckleford (DTNC)(P)
25. Newlands Batch (DTNC)(P)
26. Powerstock Common (DTNC)
27. St. Gabriel's Bank (DTNC)(P)
28. Seven Ash Common (DTNC)(P)
29. Sovell Down (DTNC)
30. Stanpit Marsh (CBC)
31. Studland Heath (NT & NCC)
32. Sutton Holms Meadow (DTNC)(P)
33. Tadnoll Heath (DTNC)
34. Thorncombe Wood (DCC)

35. Town Common (DTNC)
36. Townsend (DTNC)
37. Trigon (DTNC)(P)
38. West Bexington (DTNC)
39. Whitenothe (NT & DTNC)
40. Wool Meadows (DTNC)(P)
41. Woolsbarrow (DTNC)

Ownership or management is indicated as follows:
BBC: Bournemouth Borough Council
CBC: Christchurch Borough Council
DCC: Dorset County Council
DTNC: Dorset Trust for Nature Conservation
NCC: Nature Conservancy Council
NT: National Trust
RSPB: Royal Society for the Protection of Bird
WT: Woodland Trust

The Structure of the Orchid Flower

In any guide of this nature, directed not so much at the committed orchid enthusiast, but seeking to find new converts to the faith, it is necessary from the outset to define one's terms, and in the process to dispel a few illusions as well.

To the botanists amongst my readers, I apologise, but to many who are not acquainted with our own wild orchids, the word 'orchid' conjures up a picture of very large, exotic or bizarre flowers purchased from expensive florists, and more often associated with weddings, dinner parties or Kew Gardens. Understandably people cannot recall seeing anything remotely resembling such exotic blooms when they last walked the dog on their local piece of downland. When told that there are nearly fifty different species growing wild in the British Isles, many people's reaction is one of stunned amazement. The next words are very often, 'I wouldn't know one if I saw it.' Whilst a simple response to that statement is, 'Look at the pictures,' some explanation of the highly complex and quite distinctive structure of the orchid flower is necessary. Although there is little apparent resemblance between foreign or cultivated hybrid orchids and our own native wild species, the floral structure is basically the same. It is simply that broadly speaking the British and European wild orchids have many more, much smaller flowers clustered together on a conical or roughly cylindrical inflorescence, instead of large showy flowers strung out along a straggling stem.

There are two quite distinct features which must be present together in the same flower if it is to be classified as an orchid: the first is always readily apparent, but the second feature is not immediately obvious, and requires close inspection of the flower. Firstly, an orchid flower is invariably zygomorphic, which means that if a vertical line is drawn through the front view of the flower, both halves are identical, but a similar horizontal line produces two quite dissimilar sections.

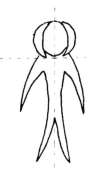

Man Orchid

This is because, although the three outer sepals and two of the inner petals are similar in appearance, the third petal is almost invariably quite different, having evolved and adapted itself in shape, and often in colour as well, to fulfil a special role in relation to the attraction of insects to the flower and facilitation of their pollination of them. The back of this third petal, the lip or labellum, is also often drawn out backwards to form a hollow tube, called the spur, which often contains visible nectar. The various devices by which the different species of orchid attract their pollinating insects will be discussed in greater detail where appropriate in the section on each individual species.

Early Spider Orchid

If zygomorphism were the only feature necessary to classify a plant as an orchid, members of the family would be easy to distinguish. It is very simple, however, to think of other zygomorphic flowers, both in the garden and in the wild: on the one hand the pansy, antirrhinum and lobelia are good examples, while on the other, members of the Broomrape and Butterwort families may bear a superficial resemblance to some orchids.

The second feature, however, is crucial, and that is the arrangement and structure of the reproductive organs. Whereas in most flowers the male pollen in the anthers is kept totally separate from the female stigma, either by means of distinct and separate organs within the same flower, or even in some cases such as the hazel by forming separate male and female flowers, in the orchid flower both sexes are incorporated into the same single structure within the flower, known as the column, of which different parts perform the male and female functions. Furthermore, whereas in most flowers the pollen grains are minute particles which readily blow loose in the breeze or shake out with any slight vibration, in the orchid the separate grains are gathered together to form pollen masses, known as pollinia, usually on some sort of stalk with a sticky pad, or viscidium, which are drawn out of the flower by means of actual physical contact by the pollinating insect.

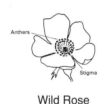

Wild Rose

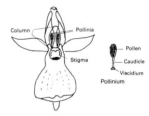

Heath Spotted Orchid

After withdrawal from the flower by the pollinator, the pollinia, firmly stuck to some portion of the insect's anatomy by the viscidium, bend forwards in order to be at the correct level to make contact with the stigma of the next flower visited. As this process takes between ten and twenty seconds, it helps to ensure a good chance of cross-pollination between different plants in the same colony:

Movement of pollinium after withdrawal

The mechanism can be readily demonstrated by the simple expedient, illustrated above, of withdrawing the pollinia with a pencil or similar object, and timing the gentle curling forwards of the slender stems. This method of pollination, although not used by every species, is the one most frequently found amongst the orchids more commonly encountered during casual rambles, and serves as a useful rule-of-thumb for placing an unknown plant in the orchid family.

The species sections which follow should enable the reader with little or no knowledge of our native wild orchids to take that basic family identification a stage further, to a correct identification of the species. The text on each species contains a verbal description, but that should always be read in conjunction with direct reference to the photographs. There is no substitute for knowing your orchids, and the aim of this book is to enable anybody to make an immediate and accurate visual identification of most if not all of the orchid species which occur regularly in Dorset.

An Introduction to the Helleborines.

A rather difficult and controversial group of orchids, the Helleborines cause almost as many problems of identification for amateur naturalists as the Dactylorchids. Even experienced botanists find great difficulty with some of the more variable and closely-related species of the *Epipactis* group. They have been the subject of a considerable volume of research in recent years, as a result of which many manuals are now seriously out of date. What V. S. Summerhayes in *Wild Orchids of Britain* (1951) described as the Pendulous-Flowered and Isle of Wight Helleborines are now recognised as varieties of the very variable Green-Flowered Helleborine, as a result of extensive research in the 1950s and 1960s by the late Dr. Donald P. Young (1953 and 1963). The Slender-Lipped Helleborine, widely regarded as a variant of the Broad-Leaved Helleborine until the 1920s, once recognised as a full species, was then recorded from a large number of localities. It later transpired as a result of Dr. Young's research that the vast majority of these records were in fact referable to the Green-Flowered Helleborine, and that the Slender-Lipped Helleborine was in fact a rarity outside the Chiltern Hills and the Cotswolds. Even now there is considerable doubt as to the true status and stage of evolution of some of the more critical species, and research is still continuing.

The Helleborines are comparatively poorly represented in Dorset: of the total of eleven so far recognised species found in the British Isles, only six occur regularly in Dorset. These are the Large White, Marsh, Broad-Leaved, Slender-Lipped, Green-Flowered and Violet Helleborines. Of these six, the last three named are decidedly rare. The Green-Flowered Helleborine is only recorded from five localities in the county, two of those having only been discovered as recently as 1985 and 1988. It is fairly widespread, though rather local, in neighbouring Hampshire, and may well be an overlooked species in Dorset. The Slender-Lipped Helleborine, on the other hand, is an extreme rarity in the two neighbouring counties: there is only one site in Hampshire, where the species was rediscovered in 1987 after a long absence, and it had apparently disappeared from at least the southern part of Wiltshire since the early 1970s, until I was fortunate enough to discover a small colony in a protected patch of ancient woodland in the same general area as its former haunts. When I first commenced investigations into Dorset records in the early 1980s, the species was recorded from three localities, at one of which I quickly established that a small but thriving colony of the Green-Flowered Helleborine had been the cause of the record: at that stage it seemed possible that the history of the Hampshire records was about to be repeated. It was three years, and many visits, before I found one plant of the rare Slender-Lipped Helleborine in flower in a hazel coppice in Cranborne Chase, and a further two years before I was able to confirm the Purbeck beechwood record with one very small weak plant in flower. Fortunately the species appears to be reasonably secure in Cranborne Chase, with seven fine plants flowering in 1985, although it must be regarded as endangered in its rather vulnerable Purbeck site. The recent dry summers (1989 and 1990) have had a detrimental effect on flowering, but it is to be hoped that that is only a temporary set back.

The Violet Helleborine has been recently rediscovered in Dorset, after an absence of records since 1926, with one good colony in hazel coppice near Sturminster Newton, and two further recent discoveries near Shaftesbury in north Dorset. It must however be regarded as a rarity in Dorset, although it is locally frequent in north-east Hampshire. There is a persistent rumour that the great rarity of this group, the Red Helleborine (*Cephalanthera rubra* (L.)Richard), has been seen at sites on the north Dorset/Somerset border since the War, but it is unfortunately quite impossible to confirm: the species is now known only from the

Gloucestershire Cotswolds, the Chilterns in Buckinghamshire, and at a recently discovered site in north Hampshire.

The remaining members of the Helleborine group, the Sword-Leaved Helleborine (*Cephalanthera longifolia* Frisch), the Dune Helleborine (*Epipactis dunensis* (Stephenson) Godfery), the Dark Red Helleborine (*Epipactis atrorubens* (Hoffman)Schultes) and Youngs Helleborine (*E. youngiana* A. J. Richards) are local and restricted rarities that do not occur in Dorset.

The Helleborines are fundamentally different from all other groups of our native orchids, being in some respects comparatively primitive in evolutionary terms, in comparison with most other members of the Orchidaceae. They also depart somewhat in appearance from the more 'normal' type of orchid plant, although in fact, this is more of an optical illusion than is actually the case, brought about by one particular feature common to most Helleborines. Unlike many British wild orchids, the leaves grow out of the tall flowering stem for most of its upward length, rather than forming a rosette at the base of the stem, or being more or less clustered around the base: the Helleborines therefore present an immediately distinctive visual impression.

The second important feature of this group requires close inspection of the flower: the lip itself is divided into two quite distinct sections, a cup-shaped inner part, known as the hypochile, and the lip-shaped outer section, known as the epichile. Variations in these two parts, and particularly in the hypochile, form a vitally important factor in the correct identification of certain of the more difficult species. The *Cephalanthera* group poses few problems of identification, but the *Epipactis* group can be extremely confusing. Great care should be taken with identification, and if in doubt — ask an expert!

Large White Helleborine (*Cephalanthera damasonium* (Miller) Druce).
Map of distribution in Dorset:

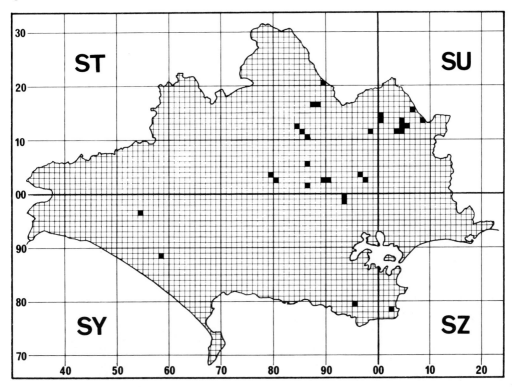

Status: fairly common in north-east Dorset, but rare in the south and west.
Flowering period:

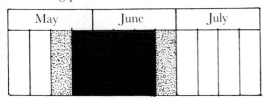

May	June	July

Habitat: E only.

Large White Helleborine (*C.damasonium*) (×3)

The Large White Helleborine is probably the commonest of the Helleborines in the southern half of the British Isles, particularly in the south-east. In Dorset, however, the species is towards the western limits of its range, and is far more frequent in the eastern half of the county. Within its range it is peculiarly characteristic of almost any gathering of beech trees, large or small, on calcareous soil, a solitary beech tree by the roadside on the chalk often providing a perfectly adequate habitat for the species. It is frequently almost the only flowering plant to be seen at some sites, particularly on very arid or stony soil, or under the deeper shade of the beeches, where it may occasionally be accompanied by the Bird's Nest Orchid. In the more open grassy or scrubby beechwoods, it may be accompanied by other beechwood orchids such as the

Broad-Leaved or other rarer Helleborines, the Greater Twayblade or the Fly Orchid. Plants in more open, lighter situations tend to be more robust than those in the deepest shade. In one rather unusual site on a north Dorset reserve it grows in some numbers in a dense thicket of sloe, hawthorn and elder bushes, where it is accompanied by the Greater Twayblade. At this location the plants are quite large, although the shade is quite deep: the Common Spotted Orchid, which can tolerate quite deep shade, grows in light scrub nearby, and on the adjacent open down, but does not penetrate the denser thicket where the Helleborines grow.

Plate 1: *C.damasonium*, Kingston, Purbeck 21.6.86.

The Large White Helleborine first comes into flower in the third week in May in an early season, and may last until late June, but is usually at its best during the first two weeks of June, a week or two later than its much

scarcer relative, the Sword-Leaved Helleborine, with which it sometimes occurs at some Hampshire sites. The Large White Helleborine can be a frustrating plant to study and photograph, because not only is the flowering period comparatively short, but both rabbits and slugs seem to be particularly partial to the young shoots and flower buds. Consequently, in many quite large colonies, comparatively few plants may be found in good flower.

The only species with which it is at all likely to be confused is the Sword-Leaved Helleborine, but the rarer species does not occur in Dorset, and where the two species do grow together, the differences are immediately apparent. The Large White Helleborine has comparatively large, creamy-white tubular flowers, which never open widely. They are few in number

Plate 2: *C.damasonium*, Badbury Rings, 29.5.88.

(usually three to ten), widely spaced out on a rather sparse flower-spike, and with very noticeable long floral bracts. The floral bracts of the Sword-Leaved Helleborine are almost non-existent, so the flower-spike is quite distinct from the leaves, a difference which is usually apparent even from some distance. The flowers of the rarer species are smaller, a purer white, and open more widely. The leaves of the Large White Helleborine are fairly short and broad, with rounded tips, whereas those of the Sword-Leaved Helleborine, as its name implies, are quite long, very narrow and acutely pointed. At a site in east Hampshire, I have seen the very rare hybrid between the two species, but these are very difficult to identify with certainty. The Sword-Leaved Helleborine is recorded from a locally well-known wood near Cranborne (Good 1984), hence the detailed descriptions of both species given here: I believe however that this is a mistaken record. The Large White Helleborine occurs in that wood in some numbers, and it takes an unusual form with smaller flowers, shorter bracts, and longer narrower leaves than those of more typical plants. I have not found the Sword-Leaved Helleborine anywhere in Dorset.

The Large White Helleborine has a limited distribution in Dorset, although it is frequent within that limited area. It can be found in most suitable patches of reasonably mature beechwood on the chalk in the northeast of the county, extending from Blandford and Wimborne, northwards and eastwards towards Shaftesbury and Cranborne, where it is most frequent. The species also occurs at two sites west and northwest of Dorchester, and at one locality in the Isle of Purbeck.

Marsh Helleborine (*Epipactis palustris* (L.)Crantz).

Status: rather uncommon, but some good sites in Dorset, where it can be locally abundant.

Plate 3: *E.palustris*, Arne 1.7.84.

Plate 4: *E.palustris*, Rockbourne, Hants. 30.6.84.

Map of distribution in Dorset:

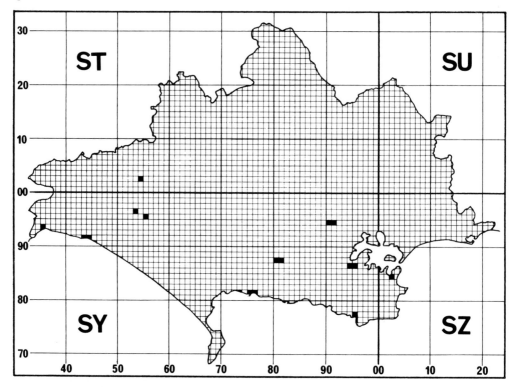

Flowering period:

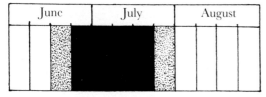

Habitat: C only in Dorset.

Marsh Helleborine *(E.palustris)* (×5)

The Marsh Helleborine, which is undoubtedly one of the most attractive of the Helleborines, is in many respects atypical of the group. Most of them, particularly in southern England, are so frequently associated with beechwoods on the chalk, that the first orchids one thinks of searching for in such sites tend to be members of this group. The Marsh Helleborine, however, as both its common and botanical names imply, is almost invariably an inhabitant of marshland, growing in a wide range of such habitat, provided that the soil or ground-water is at least neutral, if not markedly calcareous. It is never a woodland plant, always growing in more or less open situations, although it can survive in quite dense reedbeds. The species is particularly characteristic of two very distinctive types of habitat — the wet slacks of stable sand dunes, and the marshy hollows caused by the collapse of soft shale or limestone cliffs into natural terraces which hold the calcareous drainage water from the cliffs. Dune slacks are in short supply in Dorset, but crumbling shale terraces are characteristic of many parts of the Dorset coast, on the western Lias and Fuller's Earth between Abbotsbury and Lyme Regis, and also on the Kimmeridge Clay deposits between Purbeck and Portland. The Marsh Helleborine will not be found in peat bogs, which are too acidic, but may occur occasionally in the marshy fringes, where calcareous drainage water has neutralised the natural acidity of the peat, creating localised fen conditions.

Usually the Marsh Helleborine grows in localised groups covering a comparatively small area, but where it is nevertheless very numerous. This is largely due to its capacity to spread by means of underground runners, or elongated roots, and what appears to be a colony of many plants may in fact be a small number of plants throwing up a large number of flowering stems. The connecting roots do not normally wither and die off, unlike many plants which spread by means of runners, although each aerial stem is capable of an independent existence if the roots are severed. The efficiency of this form of vegetative multiplication will be readily seen, when one sees for the first time the dramatic sight of a large stand of this attractive species in full flower.

There are other features of this species that set it somewhat apart from other Helleborines: the leaves tend to be somewhat more clustered around the base of the stem than those of other species, and the flowers are large and showy in comparison with other members of the *Epipactis* group, superficially closer in size and general appearance to those of the *Cephalanthera* group. There are two quite distinctive features of this species, however, which are shared by no other Helleborine: the almost horizontal pink veins inside the hypochile are unique to the species, although they bear a passing resemblance to the green veins on the lateral sepals of the Green-Veined Orchid (*Orchis morio*). Probably the most remarkable feature, however, is the elastic hinge between the hypochile and the epichile: the hinge is springy enough to force an insect leaving the flower to fly upwards, thereby colliding with the pollinia and removing them to pollinate the next flower visited. Flower spikes will often be found to be crawling with ants: they are scavengers of the liberal nectar to be found in the hypochile, but take no part in the pollination of the flower because of its specialised mechanism.

The Marsh Helleborine first comes into flower in the latter half of June, and lasts through most of July, although it is at its best in early July. There are good colonies of the species on the coastal Lias landslips between Lyme Regis and Bridport, and also on the Kimmeridge Clay around Ringstead Bay and west of St. Albans Head. It is a rare species inland, although there are remarkable populations on the marshy calcareous verges of the chalk-based roads across the heathland south of Poole Harbour, where it grows in the company of a spectacular display of Marsh Orchids, Spotted Orchids and their hybrids.

Broad-Leaved Helleborine (*Epipactis helleborine* (L.)Crantz).
Map of distribution in Dorset:

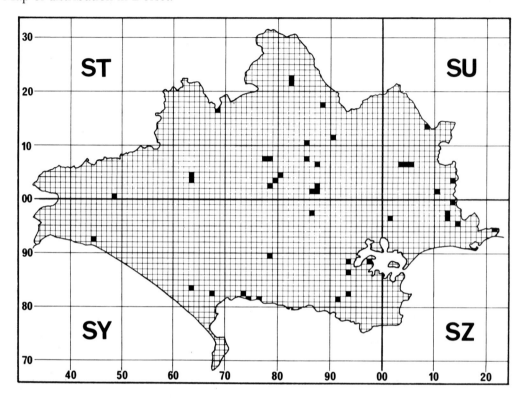

Status: fairly common, locally abundant.
Flowering period:

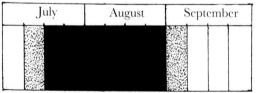

July	August	September

Habitat: E only.

Broad-Leaved Helleborine *(E.helleborine)* (×5)

The Broad-Leaved Helleborine is one of the most frequently encountered species in this group, but is also potentially one of the most confusing, as it shows more variation in size, colouring, floral shape, leaf formation and even preference of habitat, than any other Helleborine. Once the principal diagnostic features are grasped, however, little difficulty should be experienced in correctly identifying the species, provided that it is accepted that a wide range of variation is not only frequent but usual. As its common name implies, at least some of the lower leaves on the aerial stem are usually very broad, sometimes being almost as broad as they are long. They are also relatively large in comparison with those of most other Helleborines, and in good specimens may be very luxuriant. There are exceptions to every rule, but it is usually in very dark

Plate 5: *E.helleborine*, Nursling, Hants. 31.7.84.

The stem itself may be anything from 30 to 120cm in height in good specimens, and it is thus usually one of the most robust of the Helleborines. The lax flower-spike occupies anything from a third to a full half of the length of the aerial stem, sometimes with in excess of a hundred flowers. As the bottom flowers on the spike are often starting to wither by the time the upper flowers open, from the point of view of the flower photographer, in common with most members of this group, the Broad-Leaved Helleborine can be a somewhat exasperating subject, and is usually more photogenic early in its flowering period.

The flowers themselves vary enormously in size and colour, and in the minor detail of the shape of some of the floral parts. The ground colour can be anything from pale green or pale greenish-pink to a deep wine

Plate 6: *E.helleborine*, Hengistbury Head 25.8.87.

conditions that plants with small narrow leaves occur, and these can usually be recognised by floral features. The leaves are almost always a deep dull green or rich green in colour, quite unlike the purplish-green of the Violet Helleborine, the bright apple-green of the Green-Flowered Helleborine or the yellowish-green shade that is sometimes seen in the Slender-Lipped Helleborine. They are also invariably deeply veined, like those of the Slender-Lipped Helleborine. They differ from those of the rarer species, however, in that they are almost always set in three rows up the stem, thus appearing to be spread all round the stem — those of the Slender-Lipped Helleborine, in common with most other members of this group, are generally set in two opposing rows.

colour, the darker shades tending in my experience to occur in full light on wood borders. Even the palest green plants, however, invariably have at least the faintest tinge of pink or wine towards the tips of the perianth segments. The hypochile is always more or less suffused with pink, red, purple, brownish-red or wine colouring. The flowers always open widely, and the perianth segments tend to be broad and rounded, rather than long and pointed. The epichile is almost always more or less reflexed, except in newly opened flowers, so it tends to appear blunter than it really is. The greener plants with less reflexed epichiles may be mistaken for the Slender-Lipped Helleborine, but the epichile of the rarer species is invariably acutely pointed, and usually much longer than broad.

The Broad-Leaved Helleborine is widespread in Dorset, though rather local, and can be found in a wide range of habitats.

It is most frequent in the beechwoods and other mixed deciduous woods of the central chalk west and north of Blandford Forum, although it occurs in alder carr near Christchurch, under pines amongst bracken west of Ringwood, in marshy willow holts on the heathland south of Poole Harbour, on a road verge under oaks near Canford Heath (although recent road works appear to have damaged this site), and in a few isolated mixed woodland localities widely scattered in the south and west of the county. The colour-scheme, particularly of the greener plants, can be quite an effective camouflage, especially when the species occurs in a dense ground flora of brambles, nettles, bracken or other thick underbrush, as is frequently the case. In spite of its normally robust stature, therefore, it may be an overlooked species: otherwise quite unprepossessing sites may support the species, and its unexpected discovery can be a delightful surprise.

Violet Helleborine (*Epipactis purpurata* G. E. Smith)

Status: rare in Dorset (but possibly still under-recorded).
Flowering period:

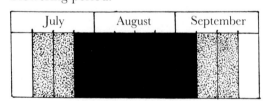

July	August	September

Habitat: E only.

Violet Helleborine *(E.purpurata)* (×4)

The Violet Helleborine was thought to be extinct in Dorset, not having been recorded in the county since 1926 (Good 1984). Two of its former sites appeared to have been destroyed, and the third so substantially altered that it was thought unlikely to recur there for many years, if at all. Happily, however, a completely new colony was found in 1986, some eight miles away from any of its previously recorded haunts, and was confirmed by the author in 1988 (Jenkinson & Hobson 1989). The interest stimulated in the species by that discovery resulted in several further finds being reported.

In 1905 and 1908 it was recorded from two sites near Cerne Abbas in west Dorset (Good 1984): one site has since been largely ploughed, although a recent D. E. R. C. record (M. J. Galliott 1990) indicates that it has been refound there. The other site is now

Map of distribution in Dorset:

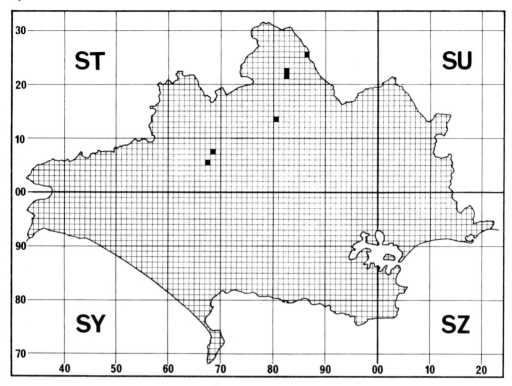

a conifer plantation. The most recent (1926) of the old records was from Duncliffe Wood, near Gillingham in north Dorset, when that wood consisted largely of mature oaks and beeches. Apart from a last vestige at the crown, most of the old trees were felled in about 1950, and much of the wood, which is now owned by the Woodland Trust, consists of relatively immature mixed oak, ash, beech and chestnut, with a dense ground cover: this appears at first sight to be unlikely habitat for the species. Recent searches of the wood, however, have revealed at least three widely separated populations of Violet Helleborine, consisting of two small groups of plants at the southern edge of the wood, and a larger population of some fifty or so plants in an ancient hazel coppice on the western flank of the hill. A further small population has also been discovered at Kingsettle Wood, northwest of Shaftesbury, just inside the county border, making a total

of four sites at which the species is still extant.

The characteristic habitat of the Violet Helleborine in Hampshire and the Chilterns is in the cathedral gloom of mature beechwoods on the chalk, particularly where there is a deep overlay of Clay-with-Flints: the root-system is very long, and requires a good depth of soil. In Hertfordshire, however, the species occurs regularly in neglected hornbeam coppices on the London Clay (Bateman 1979): an interesting feature of the two major new discoveries, at Sturminster Newton and Duncliffe Wood, is the occurrence of the species in ancient hazel coppice on the Kimmeridge Clay, in acid soil. It is therefore apparent that these sites have more in common in terms of habitat with Hertfordshire stations for the species.

The hazels at the Sturminster Newton site had not been cut for many years, but a large section was coppiced in 1986, and the helleborines were discovered on the edge of the resulting clearing. The plants are mature and have obviously been in existence for many years, but have remained undiscovered in the dense hazel thickets. It is a similar story with the larger population at Duncliffe Wood. It may be, therefore, that there are other hitherto unsuspected colonies of the Violet Helleborine in similar locations elsewhere in Dorset, but it must be regarded at the present time as a rather rare orchid in this county, and the new discoveries as most important. Fortunately, both sites are nature reserves, so the species' future prospects are excellent. Recent very dry summers (1989 and 1990) contributed to a dramatic fall in the number of flowering spikes at Sturminster Newton, but the current more typical English summer (1991) has obviously suited the plants better, as they have flowered in good numbers.

The Violet Helleborine is the latest flowering of the *Epipactis* group, being generally in good flower in August and early September in an average year, although seasonal fluctuations are frequent and may be considerable. It is not unusual to find it in flower in mid-July in a warm summer, and lasting into mid-September in a late season, when it can be contemporaneous with the Autumn Ladies' Tresses (*Spiranthes spiralis*).

One of our largest helleborines, ranging in height from 20cm to as much as 90cm in fine plants, a good colony in an otherwise bare-floored beechwood can be a dramatic sight: its size is only equalled or surpassed by exceptionally fine specimens of the Broad-Leaved or Slender-Lipped Helleborines. A feature of the species is the frequent clustering of multiple flowering-stems on one rootstock: two to four is quite normal, and many more will be seen on older plants. A single-stemmed plant may be thirty years old, and it has been said that large many-stemmed plants are 'probably hundreds of years old' (Bateman 1979). Of the forty-two rootstocks found at

Sturminster Newton in 1988, no fewer than fifteen had multiple flowering stems, and one plant had ten spikes in full flower. I have seen a plant in the Chilterns with seventeen spikes, and up to thirty-eight have been recorded.

Plate 7: *E.purpurata*, Sturminster Newton 4.8.91.

The stems are slightly downy, and the leaves, which are rather small for a helleborine, are invariably much longer than broad and are usually acutely pointed. They are often wavy-edged, and may be folded inwards along the keel, making them appear even narrower. They are occasionally variegated, i.e. longitudinally striped green and white, which may be an indication of a deficiency in chlorophyll production in the dense shade in which the species often grows: a number of such plants have occurred at Sturminster Newton, and one was found in Duncliffe Wood in 1991. The leaves are usually set in two opposing rows. It is the colour of the leaves and stem, however, that is most distinctive and diagnostic, and which gives the species its name: it can best be described as a deep dull green more or less heavily suffused with greyish-purple. The intensity of the purple colouring is very variable, even within colonies, but is usually present to some extent. The reason for this has been the subject of much debate over the years, but remains as yet unresolved: the opportunity for some research at the Sturminster Newton site may help to solve this and other questions — compared with many of our orchids, the Violet Helleborine has been the subject of remarkably little research.

The flowers are quite large in comparison with many of the helleborines, and open very widely: they are of a somewhat waxy appearance, and are generally a distinctive whitish-green or very pale apple-green in colour, sometimes very faintly tinged with rosy-pink. The hypochile, like that of the Broad-Leaved and Slender-Lipped Helleborines, always has some red colouration, but is usually much paler than either of those two species, being usually a delicate flesh-pink, mauve or pale lilac colour, and rarely the deep wine-red so often seen in the Broad-Leaved Helleborine. It is full of liquid nectar, which is very attractive to wasps: they usually pollinate this species, and I have seen a wasp so drunk on the nectar that it fell off the spike onto the ground! The epichile, which is roughly the shape of an equilateral triangle, is almost invariably strongly reflexed beneath the hypochile, making it appear rather rounded. As this happens after the flowers open, however, newly-opened flowers display more noticeably pointed epichiles: this can clearly be seen on a well open spike by comparison between the upper and lower flowers. There are usually small bosses or projections towards the base of the epichile close to its junction with the hypochile, and these are usually more noticeably suffused with rosy-pink. The overall appearance of the species is very pleasing, and it is one of the more immediately attractive members of the *Epipactis* group.

As has been discussed above, it may be that the Violet Helleborine is not so restricted in its choice of habitat as has been generally thought: searches of potentially suitable areas in Dorset may therefore prove rewarding, and any information will always be gratefully received.

Plate 8:   *E.purpurata*, Sturminster Newton 4.8.91.

Slender-Lipped Helleborine (*Epipactis leptochila* (Godfery)Godfery).
Map of distribution in Dorset:

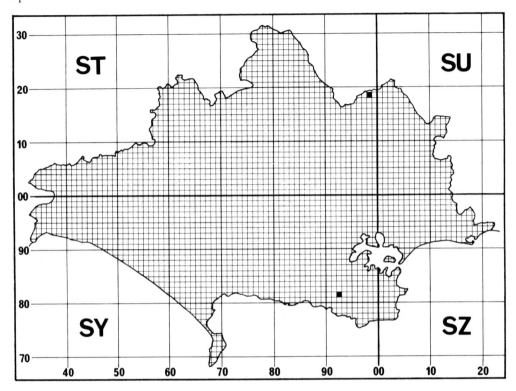

Status: very rare in Dorset — only two sites.
Flowering period:

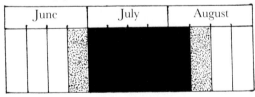

Habitat: E only.

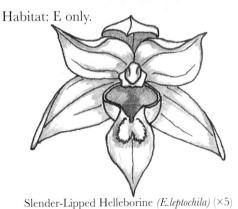

Slender-Lipped Helleborine *(E.leptochila)* (×5)

The Slender-Lipped Helleborine, also known as the Narrow-Lipped or Green-Leaved Helleborine, is the rarest member of this group to occur regularly in Dorset: between one and seven plants flower erratically in an old hazel coppice in Cranborne Chase, and a single plant has been recorded three times since 1980 in a beechwood in the Isle of Purbeck. The species had not been recorded in Hampshire since 1975, when its two known sites were felled and replanted with alien conifers: a new site just inside Hampshire near the Wiltshire border was discovered in 1987. Likewise in south Wiltshire, a former site has now disappeared, although in 1984 I discovered a small colony in a wood in the same general area (and only a short distance away from the new Hampshire site), and from which only the Broad-Leaved Helleborine had been (?) mistakenly than had been thought. Confusion between the different species of this difficult group continues to this day, and is the cause of frequent erroneous records. I cannot emphasise enough the importance of seeking experienced help to ensure accurate identification of these plants.

The problems that are apparent, particularly in this area, seem to be more as a result of a general lack of awareness of the existence of the Green-Flowered Helleborine, rather than from any real difficulty in distinguishing the two species, once the salient features are grasped. The Slender-Lipped Helleborine is in fact closer in general appearance, flower structure and leaf form to the Broad-Leaved Helleborine, and some of the widely variant forms of the commoner species may well be confused with the Slender-Lipped Helleborine. Both

Plate 9: *E.leptochila*, Sixpenny Handley 31.7.85.

Plate 10: *E.leptochila*, Sixpenny Handley 31.7.85.

recorded. The species is only locally frequent in the British Isles in the Chilterns and Cotswolds: in our area it must be regarded as an extreme rarity. One of the main problems lies in erroneous records, and over the fifty years or so since it was first recognised as a full species, it has been the cause of enormous confusion. Once recognised as a separate species from the very variable Broad-Leaved Helleborine, it was widely recorded in southern England. Then research in the 1950s and 1960s by Dr. D. P. Young (1953 and 1963) established that the vast majority of these records in fact referred to wrongly identified colonies of a hitherto barely recognised species, the Green-Flowered Helleborine. It then became apparent that the Slender-Lipped Helleborine was in fact a much rarer species are fairly robust species, with broadish lower leaves and longish narrow upper leaves, all of which are deeply veined. Those of the Slender-Lipped Helleborine however are normally set more or less in two rows, and may sometimes have a distinct yellowish tinge. The Green-Flowered Helleborine is a much smaller species, with rounded ends to the smooth apple-green wavy-edged leaves. In addition, the upper part of the stem of the Slender-Lipped Helleborine is noticeably downy, unlike that of the Green-Flowered Helleborine, which is usually hairless.

The flowers themselves are largish, generally slightly larger than those of the Broad-Leaved Helleborine, and open widely like those of the commoner plant, thus contrasting sharply with the very small, often half-closed flowers of the Green-Flowered Helleborine. They usually grow horizontally outwards from the stem, or are very slightly pendulous, creating a loose open flower-spike, quite unlike the pendulous flowers and crowded flower-spike of the Green-Flowered Helleborine. The long sharply pointed epichile is diagnostic: it is never reflexed like that of the Broad-Leaved Helleborine. Similarly the colour of the hypochile, which is always tinged with pink or wine-red, like that of the Broad-Leaved Helleborine, serves to distinguish the species from the Green-Flowered Helleborine, in which the hypochile is always greenish-white. The predominant exterior flower colour is a dull yellowish-green, although there are often pink-tinged patches or bosses towards the base of the epichile. Its flowering period is short, from mid July until mid August, but the last two weeks in July, in an average season, are the best time to see this rare plant at its best.

The Slender-Lipped Helleborine has a very restricted preference of habitat: it is typically a species of the beechwoods on the chalk, where it can grow in the deepest shade and the poorest soil with little other vegetation. The Cranborne Chase location, in dense neglected hazel coppice, is rather uncharacteristic at first sight, but conditions are actually very similar to its more accustomed habitat. The hazels are mature if they are coppiced, the species may well die out, although other more common orchids at the site would undoubtedly relish the increased light. An urgent assessment of the priorities in this case is needed, before one of our rarest orchids is lost to Dorset.

Green-Flowered Helleborine (*Epipactis phyllanthes* G. E. Smith).

Status: widespread but extremely local — five known sites, but possibly under-recorded.
Flowering period:

July		August		September	

Habitat: E only, in Dorset.

Green-Flowered Helleborine *(E.phyllanthes)* (×4)

The Green-Flowered Helleborine has been the cause of much controversy and

Map of distribution in Dorset:

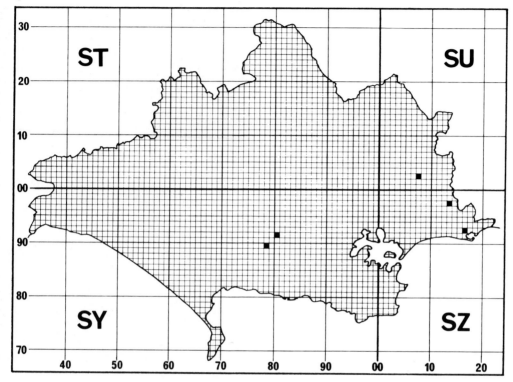

enormous confusion amongst botanists for many years. First discovered in Phillis Wood (hence its botanical name), near Westdean in Sussex in 1838 and 1839, and described by its finder, Gerard E. Smith, in a paper published in 1852, it has been largely ignored by botanists ever since, apart from one or two fascinating references to it: there is a record of it as *E.phyllanthes* in Wiltshire county records, found near Salisbury in 1876, and I have also seen it referred to rather curiously in a 1914 flora as *E.viridiflora*. The confusion started later this century, when the late Reverend Hunnybun discovered it near Ventnor in 1917: shortly afterwards it was found in a few other sites and named the Isle of Wight Helleborine (*E.vectensis*). In 1941, Mr. Charles Thomas named a similar Lancashire plant the Pendulous-Flowered Helleborine (*E. pendula*), and a further variant from south Wales the Welsh Helleborine (*E.cambrensis*).

Similar plants were reported from widely separated localities throughout the southern part of England in particular, but it was not until the late Dr. Donald P. Young (1952 and 1962) visited all the recorded locations of these plants, and quite a few more from which the Slender-Lipped Helleborine had mistakenly been recorded, that all the widely divergent reports were identified as, and collated under the heading of the long-overlooked Green-Flowered Helleborine, discovered over a century before and incomprehensibly ignored. Dr. Young then arbitrarily subdivided the species into four convenient varieties that broadly accounted for the discrepancies between the various records in terms of relatively minor but distinct variations in the shape of some floral parts. It was nevertheless accepted that these were arbitrary divisions of convenience, and that intermediate forms occurred. The original

Sussex plants were thus classified as *E.phyllanthes* var.*phyllanthes*, the Isle of Wight Helleborine became var.*vectensis*, and the Pendulous-Flowered Helleborine became var.*pendula*. The fourth subdivision, intermediate between var.*phyllanthes* and var. *vectensis*, was named var.*degenera* in response to the opinion of M. J. Godfery (1933, and see also Summerhayes 1951) that it represented a degenerate form of the species, being invariably self-pollinated in bud and withering before opening, and showing an incompletely formed lip. In fact, all varieties are self-pollinating: most plants will be found with swollen ovaries as soon as the flowers open, and are very obviously already fertilised in bud by the internal disintegration of the poorly formed reproductive parts. Some plants do not open at all, particularly in very dry seasons: such flowers are termed cleistogamous. Conversely, in exceptionally wet seasons, plants may open more widely than normal, although it is fair to say that in my experience var.*degenera* and var. *vectensis* are more often cleistogamous than either of the other two varieties.

The Green-Flowered Helleborine is fairly readily recognised: it is a rather slender plant, more delicate than most other Helleborines, being generally from about 15 to 40cm in height, with very small green flowers which hang down almost vertically. The flowers rarely open widely, and sometimes do not open at all. All the inner parts of the flower, except the often prematurely withered, brownish reproductive parts, are a pale greenish-white colour: this is one of the easiest ways of distinguishing the species, as all other Helleborines of the *Epipactis* group except the distinctive Marsh Helleborine show a hypochile that is more or less suffused with various shades of pink or red. A plant with a greenish-white hypochile, regardless of other features, will almost certainly be a Green-Flowered Helleborine.

Plate 11: *E.phyllanthes*, Moreton 1.8.84.

The species usually (though not always) has a hairless stem, which is slender and often bent through weakness. The three to five leaves are a fresh bright apple-green colour, except in the driest locations, where they may be more of a greyish-green shade. They are fairly long and rather narrow, rounded at the tips, and almost invariably wavy-edged. Their texture is rather soft and silky, or sometimes waxy, and they are very lightly veined, unlike most members of this group, in which the veining is very marked. The almost perpendicular angle at which the flowers hang on the stem produces a quite distinctive crowded appearance to the flower-spike, although there are normally comparatively few flowers on the spike: two to ten flowers is quite normal, whereas twenty or more is exceptional. The plant illustrated (Plate 11), photographed near Moreton, is the largest I have ever seen, at 57cm with nine leaves and twenty-four flowers.

The varieties of the Green-Flowered Helleborine are not too difficult to distinguish with experience, although as has been stated above, the subdivisions are arbitrary, and intermediates do occur.

Epipactis phyllanthes: varieties.

(with sepals & petals removed)

Var. *phyllanthes*: this is the nominate variety identified by Gerard Smith, and has no hypochile, so the lip is totally sepaloid. It usually has a long stalk to the anther.

Var. *degenera*: this variety has a rudimentary, shallow hypochile with little, if any, division between the two sections of the lip. It also has a long stalk to the anther.

Var. *vectensis*: the lip is perfectly formed with a distinctly separate epichile and hypochile: the epichile is noticeably longer than the hypochile, and is acutely pointed. It is rarely reflexed, and then only slightly. The stalk to the anther is short.

Var. *pendula*: the lip is perfectly formed, but the epichile is roughly equal in length to the hypochile, and is more triangular than acutely pointed. It is also usually markedly reflexed beneath the hypochile. The stalk to the anther is short. This is frequently more vigorous than the other varieties.

var. phyllanthes, Andover.

var. degenera, Salisbury.

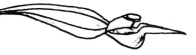

var. vectensis, Bovington.

approaching var. pendula, Christchurch.

Plate 12: *E.phyllanthes*, Nursling, Hants. 31.7.84.

The species is extremely variable, and the examples illustrated here are only specific points within a range of continuous variation. All colonies show a degree of individuality, as though they have evolved in their own way, in isolation. It has been suggested that these are relict populations of a species far more widely distributed when our islands were covered in forest: it is a curious fact, however, that nearly all the known localities for the species are more or less created by man, or show his influence to a marked degree. Road verges, tidal drains, roadside or trackside ditches, willow holts in disused gravel pits, and birch scrub in disused chalk pits all provide regular homes for the species. Recently planted beech belts and pine trees in a cleared forest car park appear equally congenial to the Green-Flowered Helleborine. It is tempting to conclude that an element of disturbance by man is essential to the species, although whether just to provoke long-dormant plants to reappear or to provide suitable habitat for a newly-evolved young species is debatable. I have observed in two colonies that flowers opening early after a period of wet weather, or in a generally wet season, tend to open more widely and display a fuller hypochile and more reflexed lip, whereas dry season plants hardly open or are cleistogamous, and retain the long pointed epichile of var.*vectensis*. Var.*pendula* is most frequent in the northwest (Lancashire and North Wales), where the climate is cooler and wetter, so this may be a significant observation. It is clear that there is still considerable scope for research into this fascinating species.

The Green-Flowered Helleborine flowers from mid-July to mid-August, the last week in July and the first week in August being the time to see it at its best in an average season. Because of the tendency of the reproductive parts of the flower to wither very early, it is not a very photogenic species: it is advisable to attempt to photograph it very early in the flowering period — but bear in mind that the flowers may not open at all.

As indicated above, the species can be found in a wide range of habitats, occurring variously under beeches, oaks, birches, pines, willows and privet bushes, although it often grows very close to water, and appears to prefer a complete ground cover of ivy. It is tolerant of heavy shade, but tends to grow better in lighter, more open situations such as wood borders or road verges through woods. It is recorded from five sites in Dorset, two near Christchurch, two near Bovington, and one plant being found in 1988 near West Moors, var. *vectensis* being the variety present at all five sites, although it is extremely variable and may sometimes approach var. *pendula* in form. Hampshire is a stronghold of the species, all four varieties occurring, although var.*phyllanthes* and var. *pendula* are very rare. Var.*vectensis* is particularly frequent in marshy willow holts along the valleys of the Rivers Test and Itchen, and as there is much similar habitat along the valleys of Dorset's rivers, the species may well be more frequent than is currently realised.

Autumn Ladies' Tresses (*Spiranthes spiralis* (L.)Chevallier).

Flowering period:

August	September	October

Status: fairly common in Dorset. Many records in the south, more local in the north and west of the county.

Habitat: D only.

Map of distribution in Dorset:

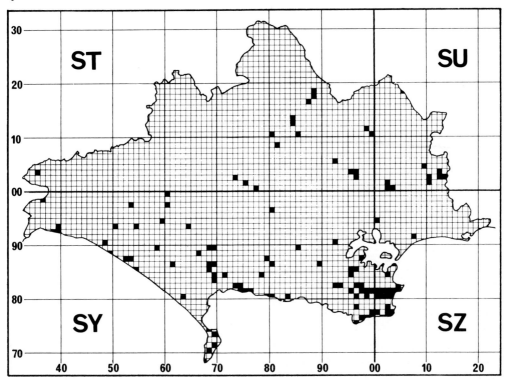

Autumn Ladies' Tresses *(S.spiralis)* (×10)

The Autumn Ladies' Tresses is the latest flowering of our orchids, being the only species which consistently flowers well into September, although the Violet Helleborine may occasionally last into early September in a late season. At first sight rather fancifully named, closer inspection of the tiny spiral flowering spikes will reveal a plait formed by the furry ovaries tightly entwined around the stem. In an average season, the species is at its best in the last week of August and the first two weeks of September, although its flowering times may be drastically affected by exceptional weather. In 1983, for example, there was a long hot dry spell in July and August: the creeping root-stocks just below the surface were apparently unable to store sufficient water to support a flower-spike, as many plants did not flower. Those that did so flowered late, a week or so after the first heavy rain for many weeks. The development of the flower-spike is extremely rapid once conditions are favourable: a hands-and-knees search of one locality on 23rd August 1983 failed to reveal the slightest trace of any plants. It rained heavily that night, and exactly a week later, the plants were up and in full flower. At the

Plate 13: *S.spiralis*, Worth Matravers 26.8.87.

recently been proved to develop from seed to flower in as little as five years. Being so tolerant, it is therefore often one of the first orchids to recolonise disturbed grassland.

It is a very attractive species, with its tiny tubular white flowers and frilly lip, set more or less in a spiral around the stem, but its size and natural camouflage are such that it is easily overlooked. It is one of our smaller orchids, often reaching no more than 5 to 8cm in height, although exceptionally robust plants in good sites may reach 15 to 20cm. In addition, the predominantly grey-green foliage, stem, ovaries and bracts blend perfectly with the colour of chalk downland turf. Close examination of the tiny leaf rosette will reveal that it is slightly to one side of the flowering stem: that is because those

other extreme, the cold wet summer of 1985 also retarded the plants, most not flowering until the first week of September. It would seem that the typical warm wet British August is best for the species, bringing it into flower as early as the third week in August.

The Autumn Ladies' Tresses, although typically a species of the shortest turf of chalk and limestone grassland, particularly favouring the close-cropped turf of ancient earthworks, is very tolerant of a wide range of soils, from the mildly acidic grassy patches across some of our heathland, through the neutral soils of old meadows, garden lawns, tennis courts and road verges, to the highly calcareous thin soils of the downs. It only appears to need a warm, well-drained site with short turf: it is one of our fastest-growing orchid species, having

Plate 14: *S.spiralis*, Ringwood, Hants. 14.9.86.

leaves are in fact those of next year's flowering spike, and will die off before the plant flowers. New buds grow each year off the creeping rhizome, a vegetative means of reproduction which explains the local nature of many small colonies of the species within large areas of suitable ground.

Although nationally the Autumn Ladies' Tresses is regarded as a rather local and uncommon species, we are particularly well-endowed in Dorset with good sites for this attractive little orchid. It is particularly frequent on the chalk ridge of the Isle of Purbeck and along the coastal limestone meadows frequented by the Early Spider Orchid. It is also frequent on Portland Bill, on the chalk south of Dorchester, and in grassy patches across the heathlands west of Ringwood. Elsewhere in the county it is locally frequent on the coastal clays southeast of Bridport, and on the western escarpment of the central and northern chalk. Sites for the May-flowering Green-Veined Orchid (*Orchis morio*) are often worth a visit in early September, as these two species are frequently associated. It will be the highlight of many a delightful September evening stroll around Badbury Rings and Fontmell Down, if your eyes are sharp enough to spot it.

Greater Twayblade (*Listera ovata* (L.)Brown).

Status: one of the commonest of British wild orchids, widespread and often abundant.

Plate 15: *L.ovata*, Avon Forest Park 3.6.88.

Plate 16: *L.ovata*, Kingston, Purbeck 21.6.86.

Map of distribution in Dorset:

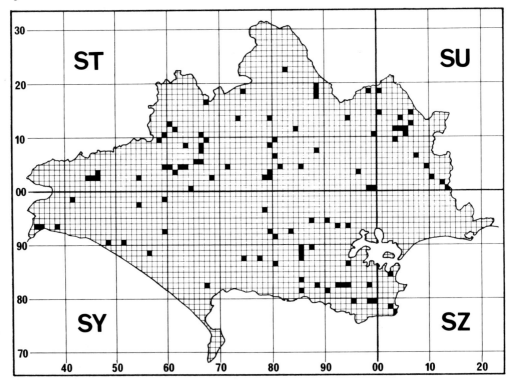

Flowering period:

May	June	July

Habitat: most frequently D & E, occasionally C, rarely A.

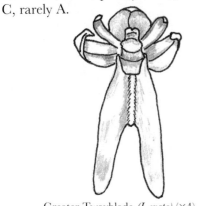

Greater Twayblade *(L.ovata)* (×4)

The Greater Twayblade is one of our commonest orchids, being not only very widespread and remarkably tolerant of a very wide range of different soils and habitats, but also frequently occurring in great abundance. It may not be readily recognised as an orchid at first, as it is often a very scruffy and unattractive plant. Its predominantly green or yellowish-green colouring often turns to a dowdy beige or buff colour late in the flowering period. As the plant begins to set seed, the flowering spike becomes elongated and untidy, and the large twin oval leaves at the base of the stem wither to a yellowish-brown colour. The root system, particularly in shallow chalk soils, seems inadequate to support the weight of the stem, which may be anything from 15 to 60cm in height, and as a result many plants lean at a perilous angle, contributing further to the untidy effect. It is probably the only orchid species which is actually capable of detracting from its environment!

The Greater Twayblade has a very long flowering period, early plants coming into flower as early as the second week in May, while late plants may last into late July. The last week in May and the first two or three weeks of June, however, are usually the best time to find it in good flower.

The species may be found in an exceptionally wide variety of habitat types. It is frequent, and often abundant, on chalk downland, where it will be found in short turf and longer grass alike, accompanied by the typical orchids of both types of grassland. It is equally at home in the deepest shade of beechwoods and hazel coppice, in company with the typical woodland orchid species. It occurs not infrequently on roadside banks, verges, and in hedgerows, and will even be found in quite wet situations in damp meadows and marshland with Marsh Orchids and the Marsh Helleborine. Although it shows a preference for calcareous soils, it is not unknown in quite acid sites on heathland, and is frequently found in the mildly acidic grassier areas of some of our heathland regions.

The flower is rather small, with a very long, strap-like twin-lobed lip: look particularly for the line of nectar which runs in a narrow channel down the centre of the lip. The flowers are a rich deep green colour when they first open, but quickly fade to a yellowish-green, and eventually to a yellowish-brown or buff colour. The very large broadly oval twin leaves at the base of the stem are diagnostic. The stem will also be found to be noticeably hairy. The pollination mechanism of this species is quite fascinating: at the base of the pollinia is a projecting structure called the rostellum. In *Listera ovata* this consists of a bag of sticky fluid which is broken on contact by a pollinating insect, and the fluid sets rapidly to cement the pollinia to that part of the insect with which it comes into contact. The interesting feature is that the bag ruptures with a miniature but noticeable explosion which is sufficient to startle the insect into flying away to another flower, thus ensuring cross-pollination, an important factor for the continuation of a strong line of regeneration in any species.

The Greater Twayblade is widespread and frequent in Dorset. There are many good sites on the chalk in Cranborne Chase, south of Shaftesbury, and west of Blandford Forum, all areas where the species is frequently very abundant, and occurs both in woodland and on downland. There are also both woodland and grassland sites in the Isle of Purbeck, on the London Clay, chalk, Greensand and Purbeck limestone of that area, and there are several localities in woodland on the London Clay east of Dorchester. The species is also common on the Oxford Clay, Greensand and chalk south and east of Yetminster in western Dorset, where it can be found in an equally wide range of habitats. On the heathland south of Poole Harbour it is abundant in places on the marshy road verges, where it grows with the Marsh Helleborine and various Marsh Orchids, and in one place it even grows in the fringe of an acid bog on Studland Heath. It has also recently been found amongst bracken under pines on the heathland west of Ringwood, and also nearby in dry acid grassland under bracken where it is accompanied by the rare Narrow-Leaved Marsh Orchid (*Dactylorhiza majalis* ssp. *traunsteinerioides*) a rare habitat for that species.

Bird's Nest Orchid (*Neottia nidus-avis* (L.)Rich.).
Map of distribution in Dorset:

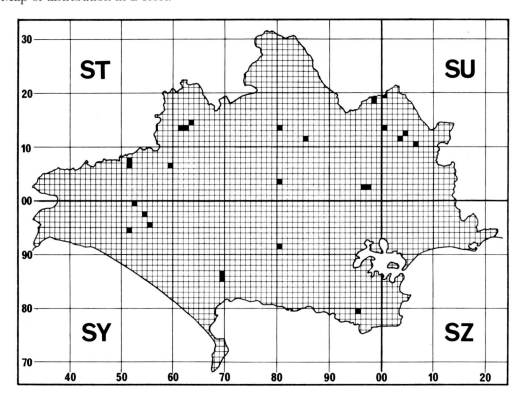

Status: widely distributed, but very local.
Flowering period:

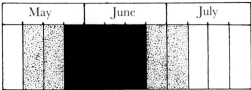

Habitat: E only.

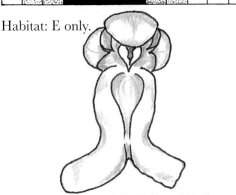

Bird's Nest Orchid *(N.nidus-avis)* (×4)

The Bird's Nest Orchid is one of a peculiar group of plants known as saprophytes. Only three saprophytic orchids grow in the British Isles, and the Bird's Nest Orchid is the only representative of the group occurring in Dorset. The other two saprophytes are the extremely rare Ghost Orchid (*Epipogium aphyllum*), which may have been seen once this century in our region, and occurs rarely in the Chilterns, and the Common Coralroot (*Corallorhiza trifida*), which only occurs in northern England and Scotland.

Most plants obtain nutrients by means of the interaction between sunlight and chlorophyll, which gives most plant life its green colouring. Saprophytes have no chlorophyll, and therefore no green colouring. They rely on a symbiotic relationship with mycorhizal fungi in the roots to obtain nutrients from rotting vegetable matter in the soil. Although most orchids rely on mycorhizal fungi to provide nutrients to enable their minute seeds to germinate, it is only in the saprophytes that this relationship is maintained into adulthood as the sole means of nourishment.

Plate 17: *N.nidus-avis*, Dordogne, France 20.5.90.

The system enables the Bird's Nest Orchid to grow in the deepest shade, typically of beechwoods, obtaining its requirements for growth from the deep leaf-litter of such woods. It is the untidy tangle of rhizomes that form the root system that gives the species its apparently inappropriate common and botanical names. The Bird's Nest Orchid is often to be found growing in nothing but a carpet of dead beech leaves, only accompanied by

various Helleborines, which are broadly speaking the only other orchids capable of survival in such low-light conditions. The species also occurs in other mixed deciduous woods, and finds the conditions in neglected hazel coppices particularly congenial.

The Bird's Nest Orchid is one of our earlier flowering species, coming into flower in early May in a good season, although adverse weather may significantly delay its flowering. It is usually at its best in late May and early June, although late-flowering plants may last through June and even into early July.

The flowering spikes are a delicate beige or honey colour, which is quite distinctive, although it can be quite difficult to see in the darkest woods, blending well with its surroundings. It is always an erect plant, and is thus readily distinguished from another

Plate 18: *N.nidus-avis*, Kingston, Purbeck 21.6.86.

saprophyte which may grow in similar situations, the Yellow Bird's Nest (*Monotropa hypopithys*), which is not an orchid at all, and has nodding flower-heads of tubular flowers. The flowers of the Bird's Nest Orchid have a quite distinctive twin-lobed lip, with outwardly curving lateral lobes, and a central channel leading to a slight depression at the base, which is often flowing with nectar. Members of the Broomrape family (*Orobanche* spp.) bear a superficial resemblance to the Bird's Nest Orchid, but invariably grow in quite different situations, and have tubular one-piece flowers quite distinct from those of the orchid.

The species is widespread in Dorset, although always local. It is most frequent in beechwoods on the chalk, though not restricted to that habitat. It occurs regularly in hazel coppices in several parts of the county, particularly on the chalk in Cranborne Chase, and on the calcareous clays of central and west Dorset. There are records from around Sherborne, Bridport, Sturminster Newton, Blandford, the Isle of Purbeck and Dorchester. It is rarely abundant, although it may be quite numerous in favoured localities. Sites which support the Bird's Nest Orchid will often be found to be havens for several other woodland orchids, particularly Helleborines, most of which flower much later in the season, and are therefore well worth revisiting in July or August.

Bog Orchid (*Hammarbya paludosa* (L.) Kuntze).

Status: very scarce, few sites and small numbers, but possibly under-recorded.
Flowering period:

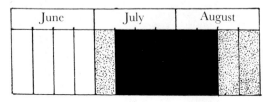

June	July	August

Habitat: B only.

Bog Orchid *(H.paludosa)* (×10)

The Bog Orchid is one of the scarcest orchids to occur regularly in Dorset. A distinctly northern species, it is more often found in the sphagnum bogs of northern England and Scotland, although it is local even there. It is regarded as an endangered species in Europe as a whole, the British Isles being its major centre of distribution. The major contributory factor in its decline is the drainage of many of its restricted bogland sites. There are nine recorded sites in Dorset, all in the valley bogs of the Tertiary sands and gravels of the Poole Basin, although it probably only occurs regularly at two or three of those. The species also occurs sporadically throughout the New Forest in Hampshire. It is never abundant at any of its sites, most often occurring as a small group of two or three plants, a 'good' colony running to a dozen or so plants. It is also decidedly erratic in its appearance from year to year, although unseasonal weather can have a drastic effect on its flowering time. It

Map of distribution in Dorset:

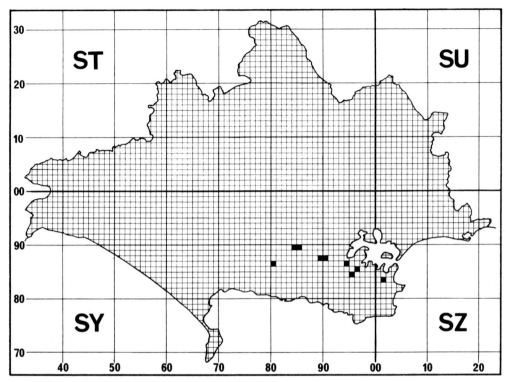

can be up to a month early in a hot summer, and equally can be up to a month late in a cool summer, although in a normal season it will be in flower in late July and early August.

The Bog Orchid is our smallest native orchid, often being no more than 2cm in height, and an exceptionally robust plant may reach 7cm in height! Couple its diminutive size with its dingy yellow-green colour, blending perfectly with the sphagnum moss and other typical vegetation of the peat bogs, and it will be appreciated just how inconspicuous this strange little orchid is. To find it, it is usually necessary to stand still and search carefully and minutely in places where ones overriding instinct is to keep moving at all costs. It favours the wettest and deepest sphagnum bogs, often growing in standing water on or between the sphagnum cushions. A tentative step from *terra firma* onto the surface of its favourite

habitat will often start a terrifying ripple effect which makes it uncomfortably apparent that the least false move on the part of the intrepid searcher is likely to precipitate him up to his neck or beyond into foul and evil-smelling mud! If he is fortunate enough to find a Bog Orchid, he must then be prepared to lie flat on his face in the mud and be bitten to death by flies in order to photograph it. Most of our orchids are a joy to search for and find: the Bog Orchid is one of the few exceptions.

It is a curious little plant, remarkable in several features, apart from its choice of habitat. As will be explained in a later section on the Pyramidal Orchid (*Anacamptis pyramidalis*) most orchids are actually 'upside down', the ovary having rotated through 180°. In the case of the Bog Orchid, the ovary twists a full 360°, leaving the tiny lip at the top of the flower. Secondly, it will be seen that there is a swelling at the base of the stem,

Plate 19: *H.paludosa*, Arne 10.7.83.

Hartland Moor, south of Poole Harbour, and also occurs occasionally further west in Wareham Forest and on Winfrith Heath. It is rather erratic in its appearance, apparently disappearing from some of its regular sites for a year or two, although wide variations in its flowering time can sometimes cause it to be overlooked in any given year. In addition, colonies can appear to move, as the surface of the bog itself may be actually mobile, and can drift several feet in a couple of years. There is little doubt, however, that the major factor in the paucity of records is the bogs where the species grows: they are not conducive to regular systematic searches, so the Bog Orchid may well be overlooked and therefore under-recorded.

known as a pseudo-bulb, a feature shared in this country only by the Fen Orchid (*Liparis loeselii*)(which does not occur in Dorset), although many exotic species have it. It is thought that the pseudobulb stores water and nutrients which enable the plant to survive periods of drought. The third special feature of the Bog Orchid, and one which is unique to the species, is a cluster of minute buds, or bulbils, along the upper rim of each leaf. These can break off and develop into new plants, an alternative method of regeneration which is shared by no other British species. The bulbils, like the plant's seeds, appear to float, and may be capable of being carried some distance away from the parent plant on the ground water flushing through the very wet sphagnum bogs favoured by the species.

The Bog Orchid would appear to be a rare orchid in Dorset: it occurs regularly at two or three sites on Slepe Heath and

Plate 20: *H.paludosa*, New Forest, Hants. 7.7.84.

Musk Orchid (*Herminium monorchis* (L.)Brown).
Map of distribution in Dorset:

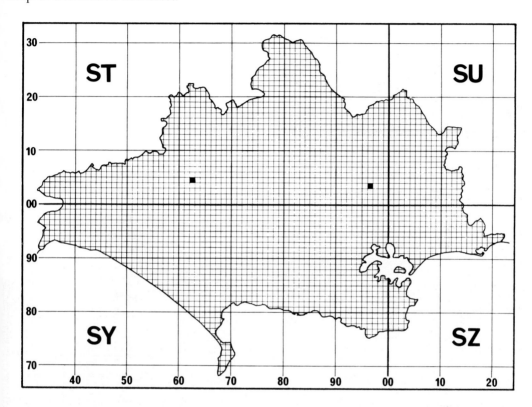

Status: very rare in Dorset: two sites only.
Flowering period:

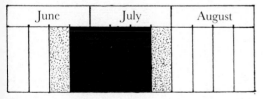

Habitat: D only.

Musk Orchid *(H.monorchis)* (×6)

The Musk Orchid nationally, wherever it occurs, is always a scarce and local species, although in a good locality and favourable season, it may be very abundant. Its appearance is rather erratic, numbers fluctuating considerably from year to year in any given locality. It may even completely disappear from a site for some years, and then reappear in good numbers. The species does however persist tenaciously at a site for many years, once firmly established and left undisturbed. Hundreds of flowering spikes may tinge a few square yards of ground yellow, while on similar and equally suitable ground for many miles around the Musk Orchid is not to be found. The species reproduces readily underground by means of long spreading rhizomes, in addition to the more usual form of sexual reproduction, so the species may often be very abundant within a very confined area.

Plate 21: *H.monorchis*, Winchester, Hants. 4.7.83.

It flowers during the last two weeks of June and most of July, but is generally at its best in late June and early July. One of the smallest of our native orchids, it requires the shortest of downland turf for continued survival, and will usually be accompanied by other more common short-turf orchid species. The Musk Orchid can be as small as 2cm in height, although 5 to 10cm is more usual: exceptional plants may reach 20cm. Its diminutive stature and delicate greenish-yellow colouring conspire to make it an easily overlooked species, particularly in very small colonies. It will be found, however, that once having spotted a plant, ones eyes become attuned to it and many more plants become apparent where none

had been noticed before. Because of its ability to reproduce by vegetative means, it rarely occurs as a solitary plant, so further searches, perhaps a week or so later, will usually be rewarded.

The Musk Orchid is restricted to the chalk in southern England, apart from an area of Oolitic limestone in Gloucestershire. In common with several of the chalk downland short-turf orchids, it has a particular predilection for the ancient springy turf of prehistoric earthworks, although it also frequently occurs on the spoil heaps of old lime workings.

Plate 22: *H.monorchis*, Winchester, Hants. 4.7.83.

It is virtually impossible to confuse the Musk Orchid with any other species: its small size and pale yellow or yellowish-green colouring are usually diagnostic. The flower spike is very slender, and the individual blooms, which are minute, will be found on close examination to be almost tubular in shape, like a tiny partially-closed hand, with the perianth segments forming the outstretched fingers, creating an overall spiky effect to the inflorescence. Its common name is something of a misnomer, as it smells more of honey than musk.

The Musk Orchid occurs at only two sites in Dorset. At one site on the north-western escarpment of the chalk near Cerne Abbas, its appearance is rather erratic: in recent years it has flowered in small numbers on alternate years. Six plants were seen there in July 1990, after a relatively long absence of records, which serves to underline its habit of sporadic appearances at known sites, especially where colonies are very small. In a very exciting recent discovery, fourteen plants were found, in two small groups about 300 metres apart, on a chalk grassland nature reserve near Wimborne. These plants were seen in 1990, but have not so far reappeared this year (July 1991). It is to be hoped, however, that this rare orchid has found a second permanent home in Dorset. There are some good colonies in Hampshire, such as those on old spoil-heaps near Alton where it is abundant, and on ancient earthworks near Winchester, where a small colony has persisted for many years, although that site is threatened by the planned new motorway extension. The species also occurs sporadically across the range of chalk hills of south Wiltshire: it may be that in the future the Musk Orchid may be discovered at suitable sites in north-east Dorset, having spread from Wiltshire stations, which in one or two cases are only just over the border. The diligent searcher may well be rewarded.

Frog Orchid (*Coeloglossum viride* (L.)Hartman).

Status: uncommon. Apart from one southern site, is restricted to the north-eastern chalk.

Plate 23: *C.viride*, Cranborne 26.7.85.

Plate 24: *C.viride*, Cranborne 26.7.85.

Map of distribution in Dorset:

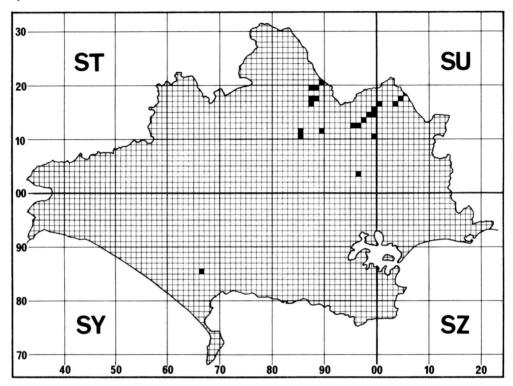

Flowering period:

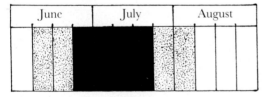

Habitat: D only.

Frog Orchid *(C.viride)* (×4)

The Frog Orchid cannot be classed a common species, although it may be locally abundant. On many apparently suitable sites it is not to be found, but may occur in good numbers on similar ground only a short distance away. Being usually small in stature, and green or greenish-brown in colour, it is an insignificant orchid and is easily overlooked. Its rather unusual appearance bears at first sight little resemblance to a frog, unlike many more obviously aptly-named orchids. The use, however, of a little imagination on the close-up photograph (Plate 24) will reveal a little frog poised at the point of leaping, with the reflexed lip forming its back legs outstretched in imminent flight.

The species flowers in the latter half of June and throughout most of July, although it is at its best in the last week of June and the first two weeks of July in an average season. Later in July, and even into August, the Frog Orchid may give the appearance of being in good flower, but closer inspection will reveal that the lip has withered and turned dark brown, although the outer perianth segments remain green or greenish-brown well into August, even after seed has been set and the ovaries are well swollen.

Its characteristic habitat is the very short springy turf of the steeper chalk downland slopes, and it particularly favours the long-established turf of ancient earthworks. Its small stature is unsuited for survival in longer grass or scrub: it is usually only 7 to 15cm in height, though exceptional plants may reach 25 to 30cm in longer grass. It will almost invariably be found, however, that on such occasions it grows in shorter turf nearby, and can reasonably be assumed to have been overtaken by the outward spread of coarser grasses, and is engaged in a desperate struggle for survival. It will often be found that a locality for the Frog Orchid, if revisited in late August or early September, will also support a colony of the Autumn Ladies' Tresses, another diminutive species typical of such sites. Very occasionally, one may even be fortunate enough to find a colony of the scarce Musk Orchid, an elusive inhabitant of the shortest turf of the chalk downs.

It is virtually impossible to confuse the Frog Orchid with any other species: its overall greenish colouring, small stature, and reflexed strap-like lip are quite distinctive. The small rosettes of leaves appear first in the autumn, and their tight little deep green clusters will often be found alongside seeded spikes, when the nearby Autumn Ladies' Tresses are in full flower.

Apart from two isolated colonies near Dorchester and Wimborne, the Frog Orchid is virtually restricted to the chalk grassland of Cranborne Chase and the northern end of the western escarpment near Shaftesbury. It is always a very local species even in these areas, although it may occur in good numbers in favoured localities. It must however be regarded as a rather scarce orchid in Dorset, although there is always the possibility that such an insignificant and elusive species has escaped detection, and is therefore under-recorded in the south and southwest of the county. New records would be very welcome, and it may well be that the species is not as scarce as it would appear. There is much suitable ground for the Frog Orchid in southern areas of Dorset, although climatic influence may be a contributory factor to its restricted distribution. The species is nationally more frequent in the north, occurring up to a considerable altitude in the mountains: northern areas of Dorset are slightly cooler than the south and west in mean temperature (Good 1948).

Fragrant Orchid (*Gymnadenia conopsea* (L.)Brown).

Flowering period:

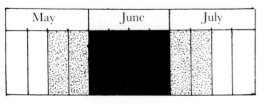

Status: not quite as common as the Pyramidal Orchid, but still widespread in Dorset, with some good colonies.

Habitat: A, B, C & D.

Map of distribution in Dorset:

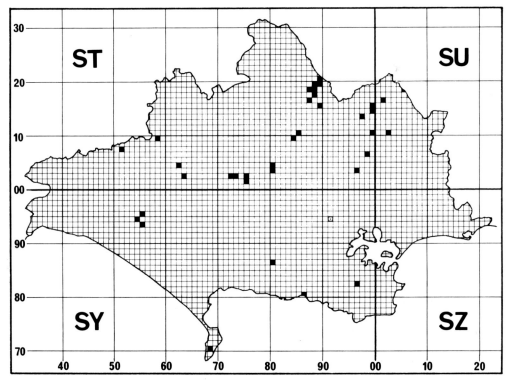

· var.*densiflora*

Fragrant Orchid *(G.conopsea)* (×3)

The Fragrant Orchid, though not so frequently encountered as the Pyramidal Orchid, is nevertheless a fairly common species in Dorset, being well represented with good colonies throughout the chalk grassland areas. It may be locally abundant, although enormous fluctuations in numbers from year to year in the same locality are common. With the exception of two sites on heathland, one on the London Clay, two on the Cornbrash and one on Portland limestone, it is restricted to the chalk, and is a typical species of the open chalk downs. It favours shorter turf, but may occasionally occur in longer grass, when it can be a very robust species.

It flowers from late May to early July, although it is at its best in the first three weeks of June. It commonly occurs with other chalk downland orchids, such as Common Spotted, Bee, Frog, Pyramidal, Musk, Burnt and Greater Butterfly Orchids, and Greater Twayblade, whose flowering periods overlap or are concurrent with that of the Fragrant Orchid. The combined display at a good site and in a favourable season, when most or all of these species are

Plate 25: *G.conopsea*, Fontmell Down 17.6.90.

Plate 26: *G.conopsea*, Fontmell Down 17.6.90.

Plate 27: Ssp.*densiflora*, Rockbourne, Hants. 30.6.84

Plate 28: Ssp.*borealis*, New Forest, Hants. 24.6.86.

in flower together in profusion is one of the great thrills of discovery when exploring the chalk downs of our region. The fragrance that gives the species its name is deliciously sweet, said to be variously like that of lilac or carnations, and is also extremely powerful: when the species occurs in abundance, the effect is quite remarkable, the whole area of downland being redolent with the scent.

In addition to the heavy scent, another remarkable feature of the Fragrant Orchid is the very long and semi-transparent curved spur, through the thin walls of which the nectar can be clearly seen. The spur may sometimes be in excess of 2cm in length, a feature shared only by the spurs of the Pyramidal and Butterfly Orchids, which are always straight.

Colour variations from pale to deep magenta occur, and pure white forms are not uncommon, especially on the north Dorset downs and at one site north of Wimborne. The flower bears a superficial resemblance to that of the Pyramidal Orchid, but is readily distinguished in practice. Apart from the scent and the curved spur, it lacks the distinctive guideplates of the Pyramidal Orchid. The flowering spike is also longer and narrower, roughly cylindrical, and noticeably lax.

A form known as the Marsh Fragrant Orchid (ssp. *densiflora*) occurs within our region at one or two Hampshire sites, and at one Dorset fen near Lytchett Minster. Current records do not differentiate the types, but this form may well occur elsewhere in Dorset, as there is much suitable habitat for it. It occurs typically with Marsh Helleborine and various Marsh Orchids in fens, calcareous marshland and basic flushes, and is later flowering (July), and a much more robust plant, with a fragrance of clove or clove carnations. A northern moorland form (ssp. *borealis*) also occurs locally in the New Forest, and Dorset heathland records for the species require investigation with this form in mind. It is also clove-scented, but is a much smaller plant, with a shorter, denser spike, and smaller, less markedly three-lobed lip.

The typical form of the Fragrant Orchid occurs widely in Dorset, with particularly good colonies on the western escarpment of the chalk downs curving south and west from Shaftesbury to Batcombe. It is also frequent in the chalk grassland between Cranborne Chase and Wimborne, and occurs occasionally in Purbeck and Portland.

Pyramidal Orchid (*Anacamptis pyramidalis* (L.)Rich.).
Map of distribution in Dorset:

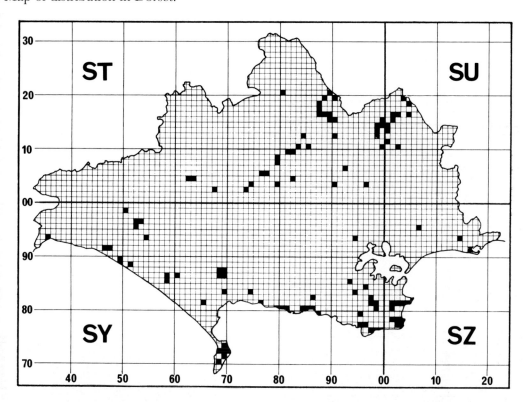

Status: fairly common, widespread and often abundant.
Flowering period:

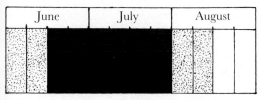

June	July	August

Habitat: D only.

Pyramidal Orchid *(A.pyramidalis)* (×3)

The Pyramidal Orchid is one of the commonest of our native orchids, occurring in almost any location where suitable habitat exists, and it is an attractive feature of much of our chalk and limestone grassland in late June and July, when many of the other downland orchids are past their best. It is frequently very abundant, and as it tends to favour the areas of longer grass on the shallow lower slopes of the downs, it is often the only orchid to be seen, punctuating the dun-coloured sea of feathery grass-heads with vivid flecks of magenta. It first comes into flower in mid-June, remaining in flower throughout July into early August, although it is at its best in late June and the first half of July in an average season: it has one of the longest flowering periods of our native orchids. The attractive deep magenta spikes retain their characteristic pyramidal shape, however, only for the earlier part of that period. As all the flowers on the spike open fully, it assumes a shape more reminiscent of the old-fashioned rounded straw beehives.

Plate 29: *A.pyramidalis*, Chapmans Pool 15.7.85.

The flowers also tend to become slightly paler in colour as the flowering period progresses, losing something of their initial impact.

Because of the closeness of the individual flowers on the spike, very occasionally an abnormal form occurs, in which the lip of each individual bloom points upwards. It is the density of the spike which sometimes inhibits the ovary from making the 180° twist characteristic of the vast majority of orchids which enables the lip to be presented as a landing place for pollinating insects. It is perhaps not surprising therefore that freaks

of this kind will be found not to have set such good seed as other normal plants in the vicinity. It is a very unusual phenomenon, but one which I have also observed in one or two other species, such as the Common and Heath Spotted Orchids.

The main distinguishing feature of the Pyramidal Orchid is the presence at the base of the lip of two guide plates, which appear to steer insects towards the nectar in the very long spur, thereby bringing them into contact with the pollinia: butterflies and moths with very long probosces are the only insects that can reach the nectar, and the pollinia's viscidia will often clasp the probing proboscis. The mechanism is certainly efficient: many spikes will be found in August with well-developed seedpods. *A. pyramidalis* is actually more closely related to the *Dactylorhiza* group than to the Fragrant

Plate 30: *A.pyramidalis*, Chapmans Pool 15.7.85.

Orchid (*Gymnadenia conopsea*) , and is more correctly placed after the Marsh Orchids in terms of botanical classification. It is felt, however, that it is actually more helpful in the field for these two species to be placed together in a guide of this nature, as they will often be found growing together on the chalk downs, and because of their rather similar colouring, may be confused by the inexperienced.

There are many good locations for the Pyramidal Orchid in Dorset. It is particularly abundant on the chalk downs from Shaftesbury southwest towards Wimborne, especially on the lower slopes of the western escarpment, and on the chalk and limestone grasslands of the Isle of Purbeck. It is also frequent on the limestone

of the Isle of Portland, and may often be found in the less marshy areas of the calcareous shale landslips of the western coastline.

A large colony on the outskirts of Bournemouth recently came under threat from industrial development, and a number of plants were moved to a site a few miles away on the edge of the Borough in grassland near Iford in the hope that they might re-establish themselves in similar soil elsewhere. Although the species is relatively common, populations within large conurbations are necessarily unusual, and developments are awaited with interest. So far the plants appear to be holding their own, and are flowering regularly.

Greater Butterfly Orchid (*Platanthera chlorantha* (Custer)Reichb.).

Status: fairly common — some good sites, may be locally abundant.

Plate 31: *P.chlorantha*, Sixpenny Handley 17.6.86.

Plate 32: *P.chlorantha*, Fontmell Down 17.6.83.

Map of distribution in Dorset:

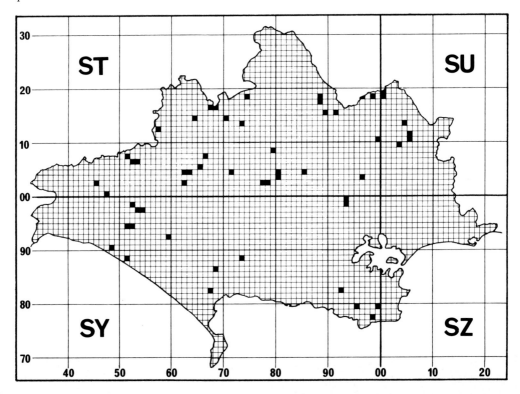

Flowering period:

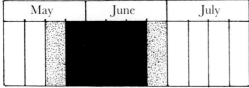

Habitat: D & E.

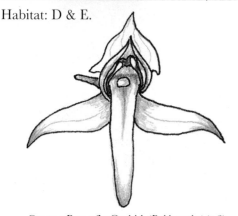

Greater Butterfly Orchid *(P.chlorantha)* (×2)

The Greater Butterfly Orchid is undoubtedly one of our most spectacular orchids: its fat creamy-white loose spikes of rather large flowers, somewhat reminiscent of hyacinths, can make a dramatic display, especially where the orchid occurs in large numbers, as it may do locally on occasion. The rich sweet fragrance is extremely powerful, and may often be noticed from a considerable distance, long before the plants themselves have been spotted. The unmistakable perfume hanging heavy in the air of a warm summer evening is an unforgettable experience.

It is invariably a very conspicuous plant: the flowering stem may sometimes reach as much as 60cm in height, although 30 to 45cm is more usual. The inflorescence occupies some 15 to 20cm of that length, and may be as much as 10cm in breadth. The broadish elliptical leaves, 10 to 15cm in length, with blunt rounded tips, are very shiny, and set in an opposing pair at the base of the stem, often lying flat on the ground. They are quite distinctive, and are readily identifiable even in the absence of a flowering spike, whether on barren plants in woods too dark to allow it to flower, or late in the season, long after the flowers have set seed and the stem withered away. The Greater Butterfly Orchid is almost always noticeably more robust than its relative, the Lesser Butterfly Orchid, though in practice there is little likelihood of confusion. The Lesser Butterfly Orchid is markedly scarcer, and in the south of England at least the two species rarely grow together, tending to favour quite different types of habitat.

The Greater Butterfly Orchid is fairly catholic in its taste of habitat, so long as the soil is calcareous: it never occurs on acid soils, being largely replaced on such soils by its smaller relative. It is frequently an inhabitant of the longer grass of open chalk downland, particularly amongst thick scrub and bushes. It is tolerant of a considerable degree of shade, and occurs regularly in beechwoods or other mixed deciduous woodland. It is particularly characteristic of hazel coppice, although if neglected the hazels may cast too deep a shade for the orchid to flower. Newly-cut hazel coppice can often produce a dramatic display of flowering spikes, the increase in light benefitting the species in the same way as the Early Purple Orchid, with which it often occurs. In similar fashion, the recent clearance of scrub on Badbury Rings created conditions ideal for plants which had lain dormant for many years: dozens of plants flowered, where two or three had been more usual.

It first comes into flower in the last week of May, and is in good flower for most of June, although it is at its best during the first two weeks of June, a week or two earlier than the Lesser Butterfly Orchid, another helpful point of distinction. If in any doubt as to a correct identification, look closely at the pollinia: the differences can be clearly seen in the close-up photographs (Plates 32 & 34). The pollinia are curved and set wide apart in the Greater Butterfly, but are vertical and set close together and parallel in the Lesser Butterfly Orchid.

Dorset is particularly well-endowed with good sites for this attractive orchid — neighbouring Hampshire and Wiltshire are rather less fortunate, as the species is rather local in those counties. In Dorset it occurs in abundance on the northern chalk near Shaftesbury, and in hazel coppice in Cranborne Chase, and is also frequent on the downs and in the woods of the central chalk west of Blandford Forum. There are several records on rough pasture and in coppices on the Brickearth northeast of Bridport, and it also occurs on the Oolite and Cornbrash along the Somerset border. It is an occasional find on the Isle of Purbeck, with a particularly fine colony near Kingston, but is rarely as abundant on Purbeck as elsewhere in the county. Because of its equal taste for downland and woodland habitat, it may be accompanied by a wide range of other orchid species, from the true downland species such as Bee, Fragrant and Burnt Orchids, to the true woodland orchids such as the Helleborines and the Bird's Nest Orchid in its shadier sites.

Lesser Butterfly Orchid (*Platanthera bifolia* (L.)Rich.).
Map of distribution in Dorset:

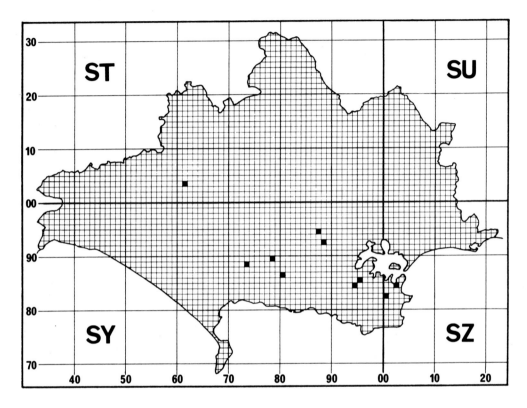

Status: very scarce and local, usually in small numbers.
Flowering period:

May	June	July

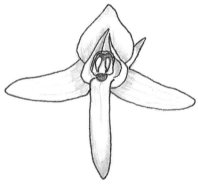

Habitat: usually A, rarely B in this area. Nationally frequent in C, and occasional in D & E.

Lesser Butterfly Orchid *(P.bifolia)* (×2½)

The Lesser Butterfly Orchid, in many respects a smaller version of the Greater Butterfly Orchid, nevertheless differs from it in several important respects. Firstly, it is a much scarcer species in this area, occurring sporadically across the heathland south and west of Poole Harbour, as far west as Knighton Heath, and at one other location near Lytchett Matravers. With the exception of one site in northwest Dorset, which is on leached Plateau Gravel on top of chalk, all records are on the acid Tertiary sands and gravels of the Poole Basin, or on the neutral or mildly acidic fringes of the London Clay. The species very rarely occurs in any numbers, most records being of single plants, or of very small groups of three or four plants. There are only ten recorded sites in Dorset. It is more frequent in the New Forest in neighbouring Hampshire, although it is never a common orchid.

The second important difference from its larger relative is the Lesser Butterfly Orchid's marked preference, in this area at least, for acid soils. It is found typically nestling under bracken along wood borders

Plate 34: *P.bifolia*, New Forest, Hants. 27.6.86.

adjacent to heathland, or along the fringes of broad forest rides and firebreaks, where it is often accompanied by the Heath Spotted Orchid. It also shows a greater tolerance than the Greater Butterfly Orchid for damp soils, being occasionally found around the marshy fringes of acid bogs, accompanied by the deep-coloured form of the Early Marsh Orchid, or even, where the acidity of the peat is neutralised by calcareous drainage water or some other influence, by the Southern Marsh Orchid and the Marsh Helleborine. In the northern half of the British Isles, it is frequently found in calcareous fens, and occasionally on limestone grassland, but that is not true of this region.

As the two Butterfly Orchids rarely occur together in Southern England, little

Plate 33: *P.bifolia*, New Forest, Hants. 27.6.86.

difficulty will be experienced in practice in distinguishing the two species. Usually the habitat is sufficient indication, and flowering time is also a helpful clue, as the Lesser Butterfly Orchid flowers two or three weeks later than the Greater Butterfly. The overall appearance, however, is quite distinct: where the latter is a robust, conspicuous and exotic-looking species, the Lesser Butterfly Orchid is a delicate feathery plant, much less conspicuous, and from a distance being readily mistaken for feathery grasses. The flowers are slightly smaller, with narrower lateral sepals, and have little or no greenish colouring. The flowers have shorter stalks and therefore stand out less from the stem, so the flower spike is noticeably narrower. The difference between the relative positions of the pollinia has been described in the previous section.

As indicated above, the Lesser Butterfly Orchid flowers rather later than its larger relative, rarely coming into flower before the second week in June, and being at its best in the latter half of June. In a late season it may last into early July, long after the Greater Butterfly Orchid has set seed. A useful tip in looking for the Lesser Butterfly Orchid, however, because of its tendency to grow under bracken, is to start searching for it in May, before the bracken has reached its full growth. The twin strap-like leaves and young budding flower stems are much easier to spot when the bracken is still in bud, but mark the spot well, because they are surprisingly difficult to find again later, even when in full flower.

Like the Greater Butterfly Orchid, the Lesser Butterfly is a very fragrant species, although the scent is not quite as powerful, and it is more noticeable in the evening, when the long-probosced moths which pollinate it are on the wing. One of our most attractive orchids, it is a rare delight to find.

Bee Orchid (*Ophrys apifera* Hudson).

Status: rather uncommon, occasionally locally abundant.
Flowering period:

June	July	August

Habitat: D only.

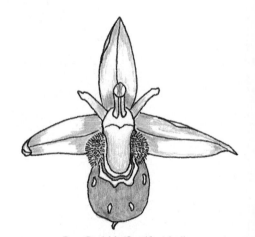

Bee Orchid *(O.apifera)* (×4)

The Bee Orchid is perhaps the best known of all our native orchids, and yet still provides one of the greatest thrills even to the naturalist who has seen it in the same spot

Map of distribution in Dorset:

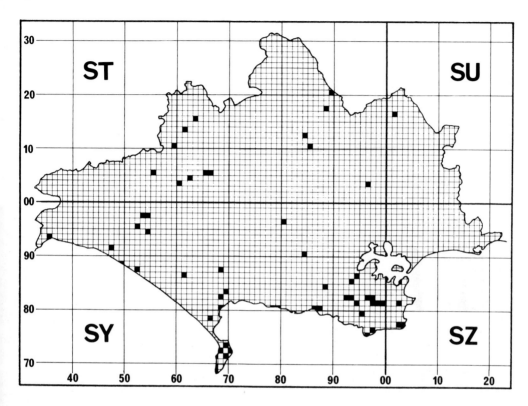

year after year for many years. The strange but beautiful flowers bear an uncanny resemblance to a large bumble-bee visiting a small pink lily, and it is apparent that the orchid has evolved in that form for a purpose: many *Ophrys* species in the Mediterranean, where the genus is most frequent, produce pheromones attractive to certain species of bees and wasps. The appearance of the orchids encourages the male insects to attempt to copulate with the flower, thus achieving pollination, a process known as pseudo-copulation. In this country, however, the Bee Orchid usually pollinates itself very efficiently by the simple process of the pollinia on their long thin stalks falling out of the small pockets on the column and swinging in the breeze, until contact is made with the receptive stigma below.

The Bee Orchid is by no means a common plant nowadays, largely because of the wholesale destruction in modern times of ancient chalk grassland sites. In suitable sites and in a good year, however, it may be locally quite abundant. The species displays remarkable annual fluctuations in numbers of flowering plants, rather like the Fragrant Orchid. An explanation that has been volunteered by some authorities is that it is a monocarpic species, that is to say once having flowered and set seed, the plant dies. This myth has been encouraged to some extent by the fact that the species in the British Isles is towards the northern limit of its European distribution, and thus presumed to be under some pressure from inclement weather. Recent studies, however, some actually conducted in Dorset, have proved that individual plants flower for

Plate 35: *O.apifera*, Fontmell Down 17.6.90.

usually withered and set seed, a feature that makes it a less than ideal species for the flower photographer. Abnormal flowers are not unusual, one type known as the Wasp Orchid (*Ophrys apifera* var. *trollii*), which has a long pointed lip, being sufficiently consistent in some localities to merit varietal status. It is not a separate species, however, and I have even seen one plant on a Dorset reserve which had abnormal lower flowers on the spike, approximating to var. *trollii*, and relatively normal flowers higher up the spike.

Plate 36: *O.apifera*, Fontmell Down 17.6.90.

several successive years, some authorities suggesting an average life-span of eight to ten years for flowering plants. The somewhat exasperating inconsistency of its appearance from year to year in most of its stations, whatever the explanation may be, is perhaps part of the species' fascination to the nature-lover, and certainly adds to the thrill of finding it, particularly in abundance in a good season.

The Bee Orchid flowers from mid-June onwards, throughout July, but is at its best in late June and early July. A feature of the species is that the loosely spaced flowers, usually between three and ten, on the spike are rarely all in flower at once. The bottom flowers open first, and by the time the topmost flowers have opened, particularly on a long spike, the lowest flowers have

Although typically a species of the shortest turf on the chalk and limestone, with several good sites on the northern downs, the southern central chalk and on the chalk and limestone of Purbeck and Portland, it also occurs on the Fuller's Earth south of

Sherborne and east of Bridport. The Bee Orchid is known to flourish on stable sand-dunes, which contain a significant proportion of lime from broken sea-shells, although I have not so far found it on the dunes at Studland, which is the only major dune system in Dorset. It does occur, however, in places across the heathland south of Poole Harbour, where chalk hardcore has been used as a base for the roads, creating artificially calcareous road verges. It also occurs in a similar location in the New Forest in Hampshire. The Bee Orchid may therefore be found in some apparently unlikely surroundings, provided only that the soil is calcareous.

Early Spider Orchid (*Ophrys sphegodes* Miller).

Status: nationally very rare and protected. Best sites in Dorset, where it may be locally abundant.

Flowering period:

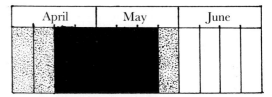

April		May		June		

Habitat: D only.

Plate 37: *O.sphegodes*, Worth Matravers 13.5.86.

Plate 38: *O.sphegodes*, Dancing Ledge 29.4.84.

Map of distribution in Dorset:

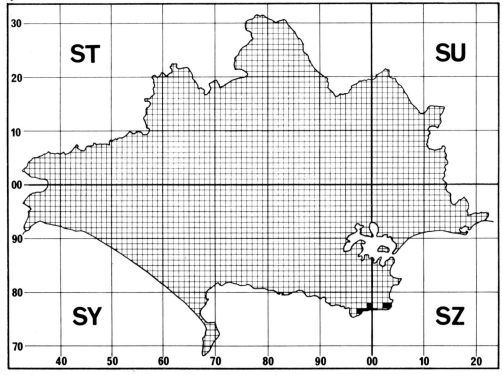

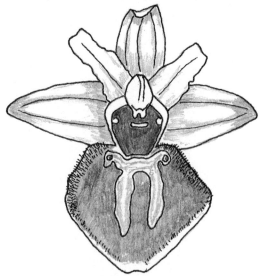

Early Spider Orchid *(O.sphegodes)* (×4)

The Early Spider Orchid is one of our rarest orchids, only occurring in the British Isles in Kent, Sussex and Dorset, although there are old records for Oxfordshire, Suffolk, Hampshire and the Isle of Wight. It is very much a Mediterranean species, and is at the northernmost limit of its range in the British Isles, maintaining a precarious foothold on our southernmost coastal chalk and limestone. It is the pride and joy of Dorset botanists, and with justification forms the emblem of the Dorset Trust for Nature Conservation. It is also the object in early May each year of an annual pilgrimage to the Isle of Purbeck by a vast army of interested naturalists of all persuasions. It cannot be stressed too strongly that the species' continued survival on Purbeck depends to a large extent on the responsible and considerate attitude of such visitors: a recent survey (F. Woodhead pers. comm. 1988) has indicated that a large number of flowering spikes growing close to public footpaths are picked — an offence under the Wildlife and Countryside Act, punishable with a substantial fine.

The Early Spider Orchid's best sites in the

British Isles are in Dorset: it is at best sporadic in Sussex and Kent, and never occurs in those counties in any sort of abundance. There are four main localities for the species in the Isle of Purbeck, along the coastal limestone between St. Albans Head and Durlston Head, although isolated plants or small groups of plants may be found throughout this area. At only one of these four centres does the species regularly occur in abundance, and the sight of thousands of little spikes of this diminutive but beautiful orchid dotted all over the hillside is breathtaking. It can survive only in the shortest turf of the disused quarries, earthworks, cliff ledges and sheep-grazed steep coastal meadows of the Purbeck limestone. A feature of the species is that apart from one colony in Kent all its present stations are near the sea.

The Early Spider Orchid is a rather small species in the British Isles, ranging in height from 5 to 12cm on average, with exceptional plants reaching 15 to 20cm. Continental plants are often much larger. It is a stocky, sturdy plant with a thick fleshy stem, and disproportionately large flowers of quite exotic appearance. The lip forms the large dark brown furry 'body' of the spider, and at its top centre there is always a shiny slate-grey or pewter-coloured patch, known as the *speculum*, which is in the diagnostic shape of a capital 'H' or the Greek letter 'pi'. The *speculum*, or mirror, is a feature, in various shapes, of many of the *Ophrys* family.

There are comparatively few flowers on the spike, between three and six being usual, and unfortunately the rich deep colouring of the lip fades soon after the flower opens, so it is often hard to find a full spike of flowers in pristine condition. Like the Bee Orchid, it can be a rather exasperating subject for the orchid photographer. It is impossible to mistake the Early Spider Orchid for any other species: in addition to the distinctive lip shape and markings, the sepals, like those of the Fly Orchid, are always green or yellowish-green.

The Early Spider Orchid, as its name implies, is one of our earliest flowering orchids: I have found it in flower on the 14th April, and it has been known to flower through snowdrifts in late March. In a normal season, however, it comes into flower in late April, and is at its best in the first two weeks of May. Its flowering period is short, and it has largely disappeared from its sites by early June. Its seed-setting rate seems very poor: on the Continent the same species of wasp that fertilizes the Fly Orchid also fertilizes the Early Spider Orchid. That has not been observed in this country, and may be a contributory factor to its rarity.

The Early Spider Orchid is one of our most precious assets. Do not be misled by its apparent abundance at favoured sites in Purbeck in a good year: in other years one may be hard-pressed to find half-a-dozen plants in flower, so its hold on life is at best precarious. Please look after it.

Fly Orchid (*Ophrys insectifera* L.).
Map of distribution in Dorset:

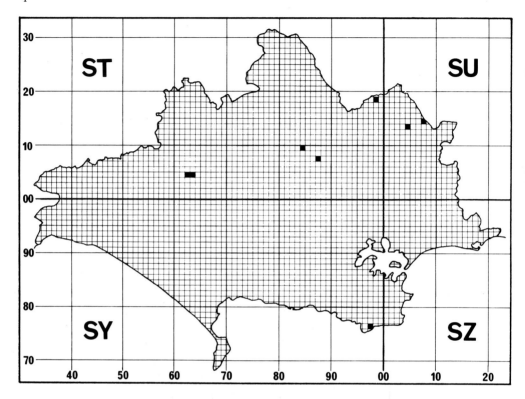

Status: scarce and local: only ten sites on record in Dorset, and rarely numerous at any location.
Flowering period:

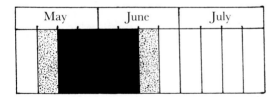

Habitat: D & E in this area. Rarely C in Wales and Ireland.

Fly Orchid *(O.insectifera)* (×5)

Plate 39: *O.insectifera*, Cranborne 2.6.84.

be found rarely on chalk downland, provided that some degree of shade is provided by scrub, bushes or longish grass. Mixed deciduous woods may support the species, and it occurs regularly in the deep shade provided by mature hazel coppice. In some Dorset localities it grows in quite a dense ground cover of ivy, amongst brambles, sapling beeches and sycamore, where it is often very difficult indeed to spot in the dappled light. Frequently one will not notice the Fly Orchid until almost on top of it, even when conducting a search specifically for the species at a known site. It is rarely abundant in any location, most often occurring as a single specimen or very small group of plants. For these reasons, the Fly Orchid may conceivably be under-recorded in Dorset, and may be more widespread than would appear from

Plate 40: *O.insectifera*, Cranborne 2.6.84.

One of the most elusive of our orchids, the Fly Orchid is also one of the most quaintly attractive, and like the Bee Orchid is always a great thrill to find, particularly for the first time. Although it is more widespread in the British Isles than the other members of the *Ophrys* family, typically a southern genus, it is never a common orchid. Furthermore, because of its natural camouflage, it is one of the more difficult orchids to find.

The species may be found in flower from about the middle of May through most of June, depending on the season, but generally has a rather short flowering period for individual plants. It is usually at its best in the last week of May and the first two weeks of June. It is most often found in the sparse ground flora of mature beechwoods, where it can tolerate quite deep shade, but may also available records. Any information regarding new sites would be greatly appreciated by the recording authorities.

A contributory factor to its scarcity is undoubtedly the poor rate of seed-setting in the species. Very few pods will be found to be swollen at the end of the flowering period. Little is known of the pollinating agents for the Fly Orchid: observations in this field are rather difficult. A small species of burrowing wasp has been observed to pollinate the flower by pseudocopulation, and it is apparent that this relies on the plant being in flower while the males are unattached, during the short period before the female wasps emerge. In a late season, therefore, when the plant comes into flower after the females are on the wing, the orchid will be ignored by the male wasps, and will not be pollinated. There is considerable scope for research in this aspect of the species, which could readily be carried out by amateurs: all that is required is time and a great deal of patience.

The Fly Orchid is a slender, delicate plant, though generally the tallest member of the *Ophrys* family in this country. It is a pale emerald green in overall colour, with a deep brown or purplish-brown velvety lip that bears a convincing resemblance to a fly alighting on a slender plant or grass stem. The small thread-like petals complete the illusion, with their uncanny likeness to antennae. The flower itself is generally much smaller than those of the other species in this group, and much less showy and conspicuous. The sepals are green, like those of the Early Spider Orchid. Those of the Bee Orchid and the extremely rare Late Spider Orchid, which does not occur in Dorset, are invariably pink.

In Dorset the Fly Orchid is most frequent on the northern central chalk, from Blandford Forum to Cranborne Chase, where it occurs variously in beechwoods, mixed woods of beech, oak and ash, and hazel coppices. It is fairly numerous at only one locally well-known beechwood near Cranborne, where between fifty and a hundred spikes may be found in a good year, although twenty or so is more usual. There is an isolated locality in woods on a western ridge of the chalk near Cerne Abbas, and one or two recorded sites in the Isle of Purbeck. It must be regarded as a rather rare species in Dorset, although diligent searches of likely areas may well prove rewarding.

Lizard Orchid (*Himantoglossum hircinum* (L.)Sprengel.).

Status: Dorset's rarest orchid: two plants recorded since 1950.
Flowering period:

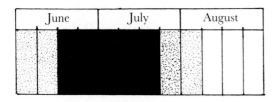

Habitat: D only.

One of the great rarities of the British flora, the occurrence of the Lizard Orchid is tantalisingly sporadic throughout the southern counties. Its only regular strong population is on stable sand dunes in Kent: apart from that site and a small population in Suffolk, its records are largely restricted to isolated single plants in a wide variety of locations, mostly on the chalk, usually separated by many miles and at irregular intervals of many years. In the early part of this century it was thought to be on the increase, with a spate of records before 1950. There was then a dramatic decline, apart

Map of distribution in Dorset:

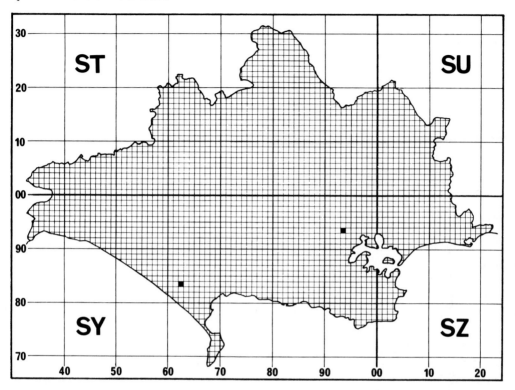

Lizard Orchid *(H.hircinum)* (×1½)

from a single plant in Hampshire up to 1950, a single plant in Dorset up to 1955, when it was dug up, and a single plant in Wiltshire which was dug up in 1967. The species then disappeared from the three counties until 1986, when it was discovered at a new location in north Hampshire. Dorset has now been equally favoured: a single plant was found in flower on a roadside verge near Lytchett Minster in 1987. The plant flowered again in 1988, but was either picked or eaten by an animal. It has flowered since in 1989 and 1990, and in 1991, four small seedlings have been observed growing around the parent plant, which has flowered again. It is to be hoped that the plant will continue to flower, with careful protection, for many more years. It may be that as a result of a slight climatic change the species is once more on the increase: a regular

Plate 41: *H.hircinum*, Lytchett Minster 28.5.89.

probably be a more apt description. In addition, the rank smell of goats that a flowering spike brings into a warm lounge is likely to be a more than sufficient penalty for an ill-advised picker, although the plant is specially protected by the Wildlife and Countryside Act, and it is against the law to pick or uproot it.

The Lizard Orchid is generally a robust plant, 30 to 45cm being quite normal, and the largest plants being considerably taller. The flower spike occupies about half the length of the stem. Its appearance is distinctive and quite unmistakeable. The

Plate 42: *H.hircinum*, Sandwich, Kent 16.7.84.

production of seed can only assist that improvement. Individual plants can be very long-lived, so their life-time production of seed may be prodigious. It seems reasonable to assume that most southern counties' sporadic records have arisen from continental wind blown seed.

Unfortunately, the rare appearances of the Lizard Orchid generate such interest that it is all too often a casualty of that very interest. Paths become worn to the plants, or groups of photographers or even television cameras clustered on roadside verges tend to attract the unwelcome attention of unscrupulous collectors. It is thought that this caused the demise of both the 1955 Dorset plant and the 1967 Wiltshire plant. It is not as though the Lizard Orchid is a particularly attractive plant: bizarre would

flowers are a greyish-green colour, with a few red spots on a white ground at the base of the lip. It is the lip which gives the plant its name, the central lobe being up to 5cm in length, narrow and strap-shaped, and bearing a fanciful resemblance to the body and tail of a lizard, with the short lateral lobes representing the back legs. The lip is tightly rolled up like a Christmas paper whistle when the flower first opens, but as the lip unfurls it often twists in a corkscrew spiral, and the lips of the whole spike stand out from the inflorescence at an angle, like the tapes of a medieval Maypole.

The species comes into flower in late June in a normal season and lasts through most of July, being at its best in early July. It may flower much sooner however in an early season: in 1989 the Lytchett Minster plant was in flower by 28th May. It tends to be rather scruffy in appearance at flowering time, because the leaves, which first develop in the autumn and are winter-green, supply the water for the developing flower spike in the summer, and are shabby or even totally withered by flowering time.

Because of its extreme rarity, the finding

of a Lizard Orchid should always be reported at once to a responsible authority, such as the local Trust for Nature Conservation, or the Nature Conservancy Council, who can take the appropriate steps to protect it. There are persistent rumours of two plants flowering on the west Dorset coast in the last couple of years (1989-1990), but there is as yet no official record of the species in the area concerned, and in the absence of detailed information, it has been impossible to confirm. Certainly the area in which the plants are rumoured to grow is suitable habitat for the species, and it may be that those who know of the plants are erring on the side of caution in an effort to prevent them suffering the same fate as the 1955 plant. It is to be hoped, however, that nearly forty years on, we live in more enlightened times: it would be a tragedy if the history of the Summer Ladies' Tresses (see p. 9) were to be repeated.

Burnt Orchid (*Orchis ustulata* L.).

Status: rare in Dorset, with only two regular sites.

Plate 43: *O.ustulata*, Martin, Hants. 29.5.83.

Plate 44: *O.ustulata*, Martin, Hants. 17.6.86.

Map of distribution in Dorset:

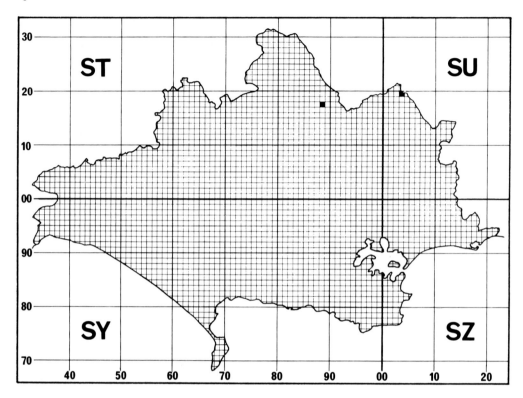

Flowering period:

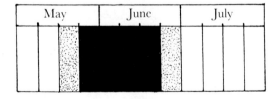

Habitat: D only.

Burnt Orchid *(O.ustulata)* (×4)

The Burnt, Burnt-Tip or Dwarf Orchid is one of the prettiest and daintiest of our native wild orchids: it is also one of the scarcest species to occur regularly in Dorset. It has been recorded from only four sites in the county, and of recent years has only occurred at two. Recent studies (Foley 1987/1990) show that it is in serious decline nationally as a species, and must be considered threatened. It is decidedly uncertain in its appearance from year to year, and tends to occur usually as a solitary plant or very small group of two or three plants, although some famous populations in other counties are still very large. Being in addition a diminutive species, from 5 to 10cm being quite normal, it is also easily overlooked.

It can flower from about the third week of May in a favourable season, and may last through most of June in a cool season. In a normal season, however, it is at its best in the fourth week of May and the first week of June. It has recently been discovered (Foley 1990) that some distinct populations flower a month or so later, although the reason for this is not yet known. The deep purplish-brown colouring of the unopened buds at the top of the flowering spike, which gives the species its common and Latin names, quickly fades as the flowering period progresses.

The species occurs in this area only on the chalk, where it favours the very shortest of downland turf: being so small in stature, it is unable to survive in competition with coarser grasses and faster-growing plants. The Burnt Orchid also appears to have a very low threshold of tolerance to interference, and it may be that windborne agricultural sprays from adjacent farmland have contributed to its decline in recent years. In any event, any disturbance of the chalk grassland soil will effectively destroy it, as it is one of the slowest growing of our native orchids. Although former estimates may be excessive, as aseptic culture has produced flowers in a much shorter time, it may take ten years or more to send up the first leaf from the rhizome, and up to sixteen years to flower. It is therefore one of the last species to colonise chalk grassland, and its presence at a site is one of the best indications of a very long unbroken history of unchanged habitat.

It is difficult to confuse the Burnt Orchid with any other species, although it is equally a difficult orchid to spot amongst the typical downland vegetation, as it blends perfectly with its environment. It is often so tiny that it is lost amidst a carpet of tiny colourful downland herbs and flowers, such as Thyme, Self-Heal, Chalk Milkwort and Bird's Foot Trefoil. The flowers are red and white, white being the ground colour of the lip, with a few pinpoint deep crimson solid spots near the base. The lip is shaped like a childish drawing of a chubby little man with long arms and short legs: the outer sepals and petals which form the hood, or head of the little man, are more or less tinged with brownish- or reddish-purple, which is very dark before and immediately after the flowers open: they become progressively paler as the flowers open fully. The Burnt Orchid is also one of the few British orchids to be strongly fragrant: it emits a quite powerful, rather sweet fragrance, said to resemble heliotrope, which it has been suggested may be attractive to day-flying moths. One might perhaps expect the spur to be longer if that were the case, however, and I have never seen any insect remove the pollinia. Godfery (1933) has observed a large fly removing pollinia on a specimen in France, but there are no records of insect visitors in Britain.

The Burnt Orchid only occurs regularly at two sites in Dorset, one on a north Dorset nature reserve, where one or two plants flower in most years, and the other as an occasional overspill across the border from a famous northwest Hampshire reserve, where it still occurs in good numbers most years. The species can be found sporadically throughout the range of chalk hills that straddles the southern border of Wiltshire and the northern borders of Hampshire and Dorset from Salisbury through Cranborne Chase towards Shaftesbury. It is rarely present in any numbers, and one cannot guarantee its appearance in any given year. It is well worth the search, however, in late May or early June in suitable places, for the reward amply repays the effort: it is one of the rare little gems of our chalk downland.

Green-Veined Orchid (*Orchis morio* L.).
Map of distribution in Dorset:

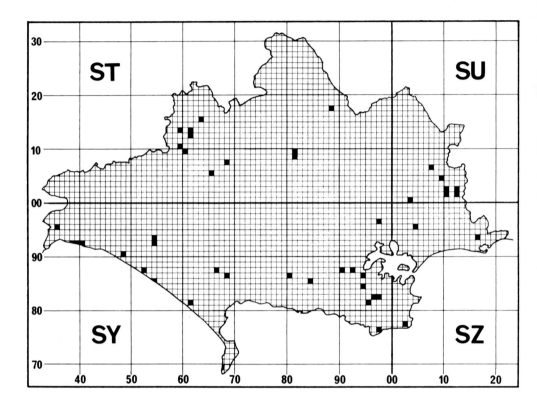

Status: now rather uncommon, but locally abundant in some good Dorset sites.
Flowering period:

April	May	June

Habitat: A & D.

Green-Veined Orchid *(O.morio)* (×3)

The Green-Veined, Green-Winged or Meadow Orchid, as it is variously called, is an important 'indicator' plant of old undisturbed and unimproved grassland. Once a common species, it is now regarded nationally as a threatened species, because of the rate of wholesale destruction of its former habitats, although Dorset as a largely rural county is still a stronghold of the species.

It flowers during May, opening in an early season towards the end of April, but more normally in the first week in May; sometimes in a late season a few spikes may last in flower into the first week or two of June. It is normally at its best, however, in the second and third weeks of May, at peak cowslip time, a species with which the Green-Veined Orchid often grows because of their similarly restricted habitat requirements. A good display of these lovely orchids with cowslips and Early Spider Orchids, an occasional occurrence in the Isle of Purbeck, is a wonderful sight.

The Green-Veined Orchid exhibits enormous variation in colour, from a rather uncommon but very beautiful pale coral pink shade, through various intermediate shades of pink, mauve, scarlet and purple

Plate 46: *O.morio*, Avon Forest Park 16.5.86.

including bicoloured pink and purple, to the more usual deep violet-purple. Pure white forms occur rather rarely. It also has rather large flowers in comparison with most of our native wild orchids, particularly in relation to its own rather diminutive stature. It normally ranges in height from about 7 to 13cm, and requires short well-grazed turf to survive, although exceptional plants may reach 25 to 30cm. At one spectacular newly notified site near Corfe Mullen all colour forms are represented, in a population of five thousand plus plants, many of which reach 40cm. It is readily distinguished from the Early Purple Orchid, which is the only species with which it is at all likely to be confused, by its generally shorter stature, larger flowers, absence of spotting on the leaves, and the presence of the characteristic

Plate 45: *O.morio*, Avon Forest Park 16.5.86.

well-defined horizontal green veins on the inside of the lateral sepals, a feature unique to the species and which gives it its common name.

Although nationally a threatened species, because of the decline of old grassland, the Green-Veined Orchid is well represented in Dorset with a number of good colonies. It is particularly frequent on areas of heathland in the east of the county, growing in local abundance in small pockets of neutral grassland probably created by antique disturbance of the largely acid sands and gravels of the western fringes of the New Forest. At one site at St. Leonards it grows in spectacular profusion, in all imaginable shades, including pure white albinos, and with many exceptionally robust plants, on the old lawns around a complex of buildings, where it is tended with loving care by the proprietary interest of gardeners and other staff. This site, the newly notified site at Corfe Mullen, and a large population at Alderney near Poole (10,000+) are probably the finest sites in the country for the species, and the Autumn Ladies' Tresses is equally abundant at the St. Leonards site later in the year. *Orchis morio* also occurs at a number of locations elsewhere in Dorset, such as on the Fullers Earth meadows around Sherborne, in grassy patches across the heathland south of Poole Harbour, on the chalk and limestone grassland of Purbeck and Portland, on chalk downland in the north of the county, and on the coastal meadows of the Jurassic clays west of Abbotsbury and Bridport. One small colony in water-meadows near Christchurch has recently been saved from the developers in a much publicised debate: a new road has just been built across the meadow, with a fence carefully erected to protect the orchids, and their presence commemorated in the name of another new road nearby.

Early Purple Orchid (*Orchis mascula* L.).

Status: fairly common, widespread throughout county.
Flowering period:

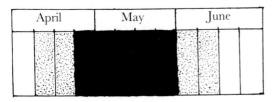

Habitat: D & E.

Early Purple Orchid *(O.mascula)* (×2)

The Early Purple Orchid is one of the earliest flowering of our orchids, coming into flower in early April in a warm spring, although the last week in April is more usual. It will sometimes last until early June in cool, shady places, although the species is usually at its best for the first two weeks in May having set seed in untidy spikes of deep purple seedpods by early June.

Map of distribution in Dorset:

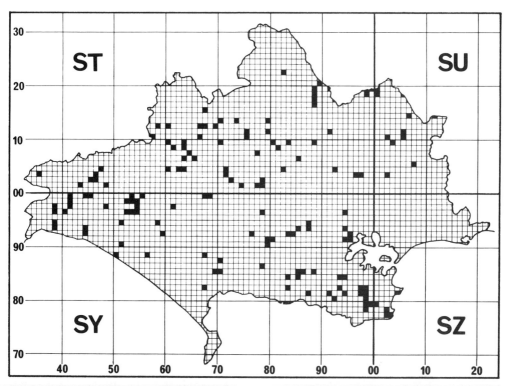

Plate 47: *O.mascula*, Bloxworth 6.5.89.   Plate 48: *O.mascula*, Fontmell Down 2.6.84.

A fairly common and widespread species, it may be locally very abundant, although in common with many of our orchids it can show marked fluctuations in numbers from year to year in any given locality. It is catholic as to its taste for suitable habitat, being equally at home in damp meadows, shady beech and oak woods, semi-open hazel coppice, wood borders and scrub, and open chalk and limestone grassland, although it tends to favour rather longer grass than many of the typical downland orchids. It occurs not only on chalky soils, but also on a wide range of clays, shales, sands and gravels, provided that they are not markedly acidic. The species does show however a marked preference for calcareous soils. It very often grows with bluebells, and the blue haze of spring-time woodlands, dotted with the vivid deep purple spikes of the orchid can be a beautiful sight.

Its deep magenta or purple colouring makes a pleasing contrast with the bluebells, and equally with cowslips which often accompany it on the chalk downs, and its characteristically long loose flower-spike and comparatively large flowers contribute to its attractive appearance. Do not be tempted, however, to pick a bunch: they have a rather unpleasant smell of cats.

The leaves are almost invariably heavily spotted with distinctive large purplish-brown round blotches, although a few unspotted plants will be found in most colonies. The spotted leaves are readily recognisable, and may frequently be found barren in woods or coppices too dark or dense to allow the plants to flower. Newly cut hazel coppice often produces a startling display of orchids, even where none had been noticed before, and it is apparent that the species, in common with the Greater Butterfly Orchid and some other species, is capable of remaining dormant for long periods awaiting suitable conditions for flowering.

The broad, glove-like upcurved spur is characteristic of the species, and is one of the principal features for identification. The Early Purple Orchid is the third of the only three species of the true *Orchis* genus to occur in Dorset, the other two being the Green-Veined Orchid and the Burnt Orchid, dealt with in the preceding sections. Other members of this group are amongst the rarest of British wild orchids, and do not occur in the county.

The species is widespread and fairly frequent throughout Dorset, as can be seen from the distribution map. It is particularly frequent, however, in mixed woodland, scrub and rough pasture on the Jurassic clays of the west and northwest of the county between Bridport and Sherborne. It also occurs frequently in the Isle of Purbeck, both on clay and limestone soils, and is not uncommon in hazel coppices and on open chalk downland around Wimborne, Blandford and Shaftesbury. It is often to be found in the old woods of Cranborne Chase, and in one particularly fine old hazel coppice, it grows in abundance, in company with the Common Spotted Orchid, the Greater Twayblade, Greater Butterfly Orchid, Bird's Nest Orchid, Fly Orchid and the very rare Slender-Lipped Helleborine. In one old oakwood near Bloxworth, pure white albinos regularly occur, in a spectacular carpet of bluebells and with numerous spikes of the normal deep purple shade.

Introduction to the Dactylorchids

The Spotted Orchids and the Marsh Orchids, described in the following sections, form the group known as the Dactylorchids, or *Dactylorhiza*, so named for the finger-like tubers of their roots. This group of orchids causes the most problems of identification for the amateur naturalist, and indeed provokes more controversy than any other even amongst the experts. Many very experienced orchid enthusiasts regard the group as too complex for serious study, largely because most of the known facts can form the basis of elliptical arguments that can be used with equal force to justify totally opposing viewpoints, and from which few firm conclusions can be drawn.

There are two major areas of difficulty which give rise to this controversy. The first is the fact that the dividing lines, or more accurately the zones of morphological discontinuity between the various types are often blurred, and studies reveal considerable overlap in distinguishing features. The most recent researches suggest that certain Marsh Orchids, known as the tetraploid Marsh Orchids (because of their chromosome count: $2n = 80$), some of which are widely regarded as separate species, should correctly be regarded as subspecies of the very variable European Broad-Leaved Marsh Orchid (*Dactylorhiza majalis*), the nominate species of which probably does not occur in its 'pure' form in the British Isles. It is apparent that there is a range of continuous variation throughout the range of distinguishing features of the four types which have hitherto been regarded as separate species, so that their retention as full species cannot be justified. Similarly, the diploid ($2n =40$) Marsh Orchids (the Early Marsh Orchid group) are almost as complex and controversial, showing an enormous range of colour variations and habitat forms. Current thinking tends to regard these as subspecies of the specific group *Dactylorhiza incarnata*, although there may be a case for the retention of a couple of them as full species. Even the Spotted Orchids, which are generally easier to distinguish, in the British Isles at least, show a range of variation which can cause considerable confusion, to the extent that it was not until fairly recently that they were recognised in this country as separate species. In Europe indeed many authorities still regard them as conspecific: the range of morphological variation is greater, and overlap is considerable, so there is a strong case supporting that school of thought.

The second problem with the Dactylorchid group as a whole is the exceptional propensity for all members of the group to hybridise with each other: most bigeneric plant hybrids are infertile, but that is not the case with Dactylorchid hybrids. All first generation hybrids are fertile, and are therefore capable of further hybridisation, either with further hybrids, or with either original parent plant. The resultant range of permutations of distinguishing characteristics is often bewildering. Consistent cross-breeding between certain 'type' plants may even occasionally create dominant hybrid swarms, with identical features, within some orchid populations, an occurrence which may give rise to the suspicion in the mind of the unwary observer that he has discovered a hitherto unknown species. Such hybrids are often more resistent to ecological change, and may survive in conditions which cause the original parents to die out. This creates a population of what may be described as 'protospecies': there is no doubt that *Dactylorhiza* as a group is in such a constant state of flux that new species, sub-species and varieties may be in the process of evolution in this way, and will await discovery, and inevitable controversy, in years to come.

As hybrid swarms reproduce and perpetuate their characteristics with constant inbreeding, they become increasingly differentiated in given localities from other colonies elsewhere: it has been suggested that it may be in just such a fashion that the so-called Leopard Marsh Orchid (*Dactylorhiza majalis* ssp.*praetermissa* var. *junialis*, formerly var.*pardalina*) has evolved. That seems unlikely, however, as the putative parent species would have to be the Southern Marsh and Common Spotted Orchids, which would give rise to hybrids with a chromosome count of $2n = $ less than 80, and the chromosome count of this controversial variety is in fact $2n = 80$. Even that is not conclusive proof, however, because of the vagaries of the movement of chromosomes in hybrid Dactylorchids which can produce tetraploid offspring of diploid parents. Herein lies one of the major problems with the group: there are very few aspects of the evolution of the Dactylorchids which can be conclusively proved. It is impossible to determine at any particular point how the variable features of the Dactylorchids are changing: some Marsh Orchids formerly regarded as separate species may be becoming more similar as the result of the perpetuation of intermediate hybrid forms, or spatially and environmentally isolated groups of plants of common origin may be becoming more distinct as the result of local influences and the absence of cross-fertilisation. Such studies as have been carried out have produced evidence to support both views, and it may be that the truth is that both forms of development are occurring simultaneously. If that is so, the problems created by this group of orchids will never be satisfactorily and permanently resolved. Any schematic resolution may therefore be only temporary, and valid only so long as the research which gives rise to it is consistent with the current morphology and status of the plants themselves. In years to come, identical research projects may well produce radically different results: all one can do is keep up to date as best one can.

Common Spotted Orchid (*Dactylorhiza fuchsii* (Druce)Soó).
Map of distribution in Dorset:

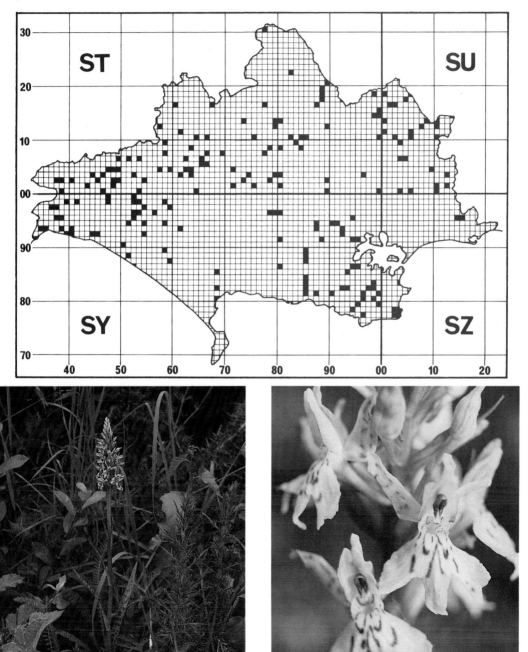

Plate 49: *D.fuchsii*, Holmsley, Hants. 4.7.85.

Plate 50: *D.fuchsii*, Colehill 4.6.91.

Status: common — widely distributed, with many sites.
Flowering period:

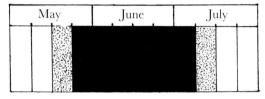

May	June	July

Habitat: common in D & E, occasional in A & C.

Common Spotted Orchid *(D.fuchsii)* (×4)

The Common Spotted Orchid is one of the commonest orchid species to be found in Dorset, with over 150 separate sites recorded within the last ten years alone. It is widespread throughout the county and is frequently abundant where found. It is extremely catholic in its taste of habitat, provided only that the soil is not markedly acidic: on acid soils the species is replaced by the Heath Spotted Orchid, although the two species may occasionally occur together on mildly acidic soils. The Common Spotted Orchid is most frequently a species of open chalk downland, where it may occur in spectacular abundance, but it will also frequently be encountered in heavy scrub and bushes, wood borders, and even in quite deep shade, particularly in beechwoods and hazel coppice on the chalk, but also in a wide range of other mixed deciduous woodland sites. The species is not uncommon in quite wet marshland, where quite robust forms

will be found with various Marsh Orchids, with which the species readily hybridises. It is also one of the first orchids to recolonise disturbed ground, and will often be found growing on road verges, roadside banks and cuttings, especially on the chalk, where it may be found growing in almost bare chalk. When heathland podzol is disturbed, either by human or animal excavation, basic mineral nutrients are brought to the surface and may create local patches of neutral or even slightly alkaline conditions: the Common Spotted Orchid may therefore flourish in otherwise rather unlikely areas.

In its wide range of different habitats, the Common Spotted Orchid shows considerable variation in size, colour, lip markings, lip shape and degree of spotting on the leaves. Although some habitat 'races' have been described (e.g. Summerhayes 1951), and certain regionalised varieties are fairly distinct (Bateman and Denholm 1989), the broad general characteristics of the species remain consistent within fairly broad guide-lines. On open chalk downland, it is typically a short sturdy plant, with heavily spotted leaves and deep purple heavily looped lip markings. In darker woodland and scrub, however, it tends to be a much taller and more spindly plant, with paler flowers and less pronounced leaf-spotting. Marshland plants, or plants in damp woodland such as willow holts or alder carr, can be very robust, with numerous broad, heavily spotted leaves, their overall appearance more nearly approaching that of the Marsh Orchids. Albinos are quite common, though most often found on chalk downland. The rather anaemic-looking woodland plants rarely produce albinos, although they are often extremely pale in colour.

Two principal features serve to distinguish this species fairly easily from the closely related Heath Spotted Orchid: firstly, the lip is invariably deeply three-lobed, with long narrow pointed lobes, roughly equal in size, although the central lobe may sometimes extend well beyond the lateral lobes. The Heath Spotted Orchid has a much broader, frilly lip, with very broadly rounded lateral lobes, and a very short central lobe that does not usually extend beyond the laterals. The second feature is the shape of the lowest leaves: in the Common Spotted Orchid these are rounded at the ends, whereas all the leaves of the Heath Spotted Orchid are acutely pointed.

The Common Spotted Orchid has been a source of some confusion over the years: the two British Spotted Orchids were not differentiated until as late as 1915, and only then in this country. On the Continent many workers still classify them both as subspecies or varieties of *D.maculata*: as they are less distinct in Europe, there is probably a strong argument for treating the Common Spotted Orchid as a subspecies rather than as a full species. As a result, many older floras classify the Common Spotted Orchid as *D.maculata*, and it is thus difficult to be confident of any but the most recent records. Nonetheless it is certainly a common species throughout Dorset, occurring in the full range of different habitats, and exhibiting a wide range of variation. Hybrids with other Dactylorchids are frequent, and there are occasional records of hybrids with other orchid species, particularly with the Fragrant Orchid. The Common Spotted Orchid is particularly common in the Isle of Purbeck, in Cranborne Chase, and in the central chalk belt from Blandford Forum extending westwards towards Beaminster. There are also good sites on the western escarpment of the northern chalk, from Blandford northwards towards Shaftesbury, and on the calcareous clays of the western Lias. There are some records of the species on heathland sites in the east of the county, and I have even seen it growing in quite acid soil under pine trees in Avon Forest Park, in a carpet of pine needles and pine cones, a most unexpected departure from its more accustomed type of habitat.

Heath Spotted Orchid (*Dactylorhiza maculata* (L.)Soó).

Status: locally common where suitable habitat exists.
Flowering period:

May	June	July

Habitat: most common on A, occasional in B & C, rare in E.

Heath Spotted Orchid *(D.maculata)* (×4)

Map of distribution in Dorset:

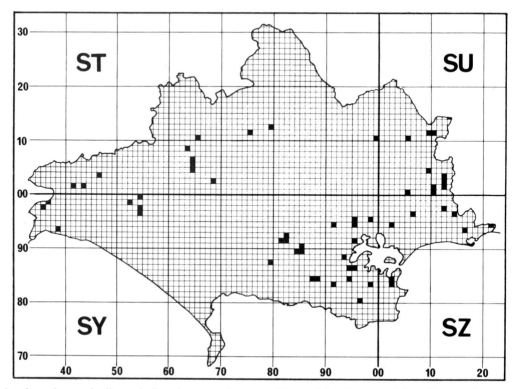

As has been indicated in the previous section, the Spotted Orchids have been subject over the years to considerable nomenclatural confusion, the form of the Heath Spotted Orchid most often encountered in the British Isles being usually classified as a subspecies (ssp.*ericetorum* (E. F. Linton) P. F. Hunt & Summerhayes) of the European *D.maculata*. The most recent studies, however (Bateman & Denholm 1989), indicate that there is no justification for retention of the numerous subdivisions of *D.maculata*, as the species exhibits a continuous range of variation across the lines of distinction between forms, so that such distinctions can be at best only arbitrary divisions of convenience, that have little or no real taxonomic value.

As its common name implies, the Heath Spotted Orchid is the most frequently occurring orchid species on acid heathland, and is most common in the New Forest in Hampshire. It extends into Dorset, however, on the western fringes of the Hampshire Basin, and is also common in the Poole Basin. It is recorded from the west of the county, where the sandy areas of the Lias and Oxford Clay have been leached and support a local heathland flora, but such records are rather more sporadic. Both Spotted Orchids will occasionally be found together in mildly acid or neutral intermediate areas of habitat, and their hybrid offspring (*Dactylorhiza × transiens*) can be quite spectacular: usually however, the relative acidity or alkalinity of the soil renders the two species mutually exclusive, and the presence of one or the other species acts as a fairly reliable soil indicator. The Heath Spotted Orchid will often be found in quite wet conditions in mildly acid marshland, damp hollows on heathland, or even in the fringes of acid bog: in such sites the species will often be accompanied by various Marsh Orchids, particularly the deep-coloured form (ssp.*pulchella*) of the Early Marsh Orchid, with which it readily and frequently hybridises.

Plate 51: *D.maculata*, Ringwood, Hants. 11.6.83.

The Heath Spotted Orchid flowers from the latter part of May, throughout June, and occasionally lasting into July in a late season: in a normal season, however, it is at its best in the first two weeks of June. When the flowers first open they are a delicate pale flesh-pink colour, but that rapidly fades to a pale pinkish-white or even almost white as the spike ages. The species may occur in such numbers in favoured locations that hundreds of square metres of heathland or rough pasture are tinted pale pinkish-white by the flower spikes.

It exhibits, in common with all the Dactylorchids, a wide range of variation in colouring, size, lip shape and markings, and degree of spotting of the leaves, but on the whole the Heath Spotted Orchid is a more delicate plant than its lime-loving relative. It is smaller and more slender than the Common Spotted Orchid, being usually 10 to 20cm in height, and noticeably thinner-stemmed. It has fewer, narrower leaves, all of which are invariably acutely pointed. The flower spike is shorter and broader, and usually more rounded than conical, while the flowers themselves are often set on the stem in a noticeable spiral, a feature completely absent from the Common Spotted Orchid. The flowers are usually paler in overall colour with less

Plate 52: *D.maculata*, Ringwood, Hants. 11.6.83.

intense lip markings, in the form of finely dotted loops, or irregular fine dots and dashes. Full loops are occasionally formed, but these are rarely so pronounced as those of the Common Spotted Orchid. The lip is broader, more rounded and less markedly three-lobed, and often exhibits a frilly, or serrated edge, to the extent that the flowers may resemble miniature ballerinas. The Heath Spotted Orchid shows equivalent variations to those of the Common Spotted Orchid in the extremes of its habitat range: the small sturdy plants are found on exposed heathland, while tall leafy plants can be found in sheltered shady sites along wood borders and amongst bracken. Strangely, though, in my experience, these more robust plants are sometimes more heavily marked and the lip more three-lobed, in some respects intermediate in form between the two species. Once the salient features of the two Spotted Orchids are grasped, however, they are not too difficult to distinguish. The situation on site may be complicated by the presence of numerous hybrids, but hybrid vigour is often a useful clue to the identification of these difficult intermediate plants.

The Diploid Marsh Orchids (*Dactylorhiza incarnata* (L.)Soó)

Status: widespread but local, rarely abundant.
Flowering period:

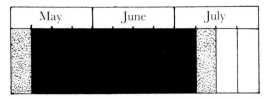

May	June	July

Habitat: A, B & C, rarely D.

Early Marsh Orchid *(D.incarnata)* (×4)

The diploid Marsh Orchids are the closely related Marsh Orchids also known as the Early Marsh Orchid group. The individual members of the group share a number of common features, but exhibit a wide range of variation, particularly in colour and habitat requirements, broadly according to subspecies. They are generally rather small, ranging in height from about 12 to 30cm, although exceptional plants may reach 60cm. The stem is hollow, rather fleshy, and often disproportionately thick, and carries from three to five shortish, erect leaves, which are rather narrow, broadest at the base, acutely pointed, strongly keeled and folded, and noticeably hooded at the tip. They are unspotted (except ssp.*cruenta*), and both leaves and stem often have a noticeable yellowish tinge which is rare in any other Marsh Orchid species.

The flower-spike is generally rather short and narrow, cylindrical in shape (except ssp.*coccinea*, which is often conical), and densely packed, with floral bracts which extend well beyond the flowers. The flowers themselves are small in comparison with most other Marsh Orchids, although those of var.*gemmana* (not so far found in Dorset) may be larger than those of small-flowered plants of the Northern Marsh Orchid. The lip usually appears deltoid, kite-shaped or diamond-shaped, with noticeably reflexed lateral lobes: this latter feature is partially diagnostic, and makes the lip appear longer

Map of distribution in Dorset:

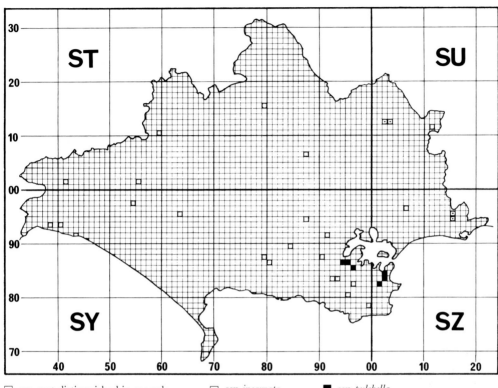

☐ ssp. not distinguished in records   ⊡ ssp.*incarnata*   ■ ssp.*pulchella*

than broad, although in fact this is not usually the case. The lip is sometimes entire (unlobed), but is more often shallowly three-lobed, the central lobe being usually no more than a small tooth. The lateral lobes are often notched. The lip markings almost always form clearly-defined double loops, a further diagnostic feature in all subspecies occurring in Dorset.

The Early Marsh Orchid, as its common name implies, is the earliest flowering of the Marsh Orchids (in Dorset at least), although that only applies to the pink ssp.*incarnata*, and flowering times vary enormously. Ssp.*incarnata* may come into flower as early as the second week in May, although late May and early June is more normal, a week or two earlier than most other Marsh Orchid species. Some sphagnum bog colonies of

ssp.*pulchella* and some dune-slack colonies of ssp. *coccinea* may flower markedly later, lasting into late June or even early July, but generally early June is the best time to catch colonies of all subspecies in good flower. Most records held at the Dorset Environmental Records Centre are not differentiated as to subspecies (hence the preponderance of indeterminate records on the distribution map). The following descriptions may help to rectify that situation in the long term.

Ssp.*incarnata*: this is the nominate race, characteristically a diagnostic pale flesh-pink colour, although there is some variation from pale pink to rose-pink, and the depth of colour of the lip-markings varies considerably from very faint to clearly defined. The floral bracts are usually green,

Plate 53: *D.incarnata* ssp. *incarnata*, Winkton 29.5.84.

Plate 54: *D.incarnata* ssp. *incarnata*, Winkton 29.5.84.

Plate 55: Ssp.*pulchella*, Studland 14.6.84.

Plate 56: Ssp.*coccinea*, Aberystwyth, Wales 14.6.86.

and the lateral lobes are markedly reflexed. It is often the most robust race (except ssp.*ochroleuca*) and is also sometimes earlier to come into flower. It is typically a plant of calcareous water-meadows and fens, and is very local in Dorset, although there are some good colonies in the meadows of the river valleys.

Ssp.*pulchella*: this is the deep reddish-purple race, most often found in sphagnum bogs or damp acid heathland, although it occasionally occurs in neutral marshland with other races. It is usually less robust, and may sometimes flower late, especially in sphagnum bogs. Usually of a vivid deep reddish-purple colour with heavy looped lip markings, pale mauve or lilac plants sometimes occur, and creamy-white or pale yellowish-white plants are usually anthocyanin-free forms of this race, and are found frequently in sphagnum bogs. These forms are frequently the cause of erroneous records for ssp.*ochroleuca*, an extremely rare

form, pale sulphur-yellow in colour, and robust with a strongly three-lobed lip, which only occurs in East Anglia. Ssp.*pulchella* is the commonest form in Dorset, being locally frequent in the Poole Basin and adjacent heathland areas.

Ssp.*coccinea*: this is the deep brick-red or crimson form found most frequently in the wet slacks of stable sand-dunes, and is included here because suitable habitat exists for it on the Studland dune system. This subspecies is particularly frequent on the dune systems of the west and northwest coasts of the British Isles, and is characterised by its distinctive colour, short stocky stem, a rather conical flower spike, and deeply anthocyanin-stained floral bracts and upper stem. I have not so far found it at Studland, but it could conceivably occur.

Other subspecies and forms of the Early Marsh Orchid are rare and extremely limited in their distribution: they do not occur in Dorset.

The Tetraploid Marsh Orchids (*Dactylorhiza majalis* (Reichenbach)P. F. Hunt & Summerhayes).

This extraordinarily difficult and confusing group of orchids presents more problems of identification than any other. It consists of four recognised divisions in this country, which is perhaps an over-simplistic approach, but is convenient for broad descriptive and recording purposes. The divisions, which are largely arbitrary, are probably best regarded as subspecies, as follows:

1) Southern Marsh Orchid (Ssp.*praetermissa* (Druce)D. M. Moore & Soó)

2) Northern Marsh Orchid (Ssp.*purpurella* (T. & T. A. Stephenson)D. M. Moore & Soó)
3) Narrow-Leaved, Wicklow, or Pugsley's Marsh Orchid (Ssp.*traunsteinerioides* (Pugsley)Bateman & Denholm)
4) Broad-Leaved, Irish, or Western Marsh Orchid (Ssp. *occidentalis* (Pugsley)P. D. Sell).

The problem with this group is that all four subspecies not only each have a number of recognised forms and varieties, but are also so variable within their respective divisions that there is a considerable degree of overlap between the divisions in terms of a number of their so-called distinguishing features, to the extent that *D.majalis* is most accurately described as a morphological continuum. It is fairly certain that the only subspecies that occurs in its 'typical' form in Dorset is the Southern Marsh Orchid, which is widespread, often abundant, and far more variable than would appear to be the case from material published to date. It is also fairly certain that the Broad-Leaved Marsh Orchid does not occur in this area: its only records in the British Isles are from Ireland, Wales, and Scotland. However, both the Northern and Narrow-Leaved Marsh Orchids have occurred in Hampshire, and a newly identified variety of the Narrow-Leaved Marsh Orchid occurs in Dorset. It is certainly possible that the Northern Marsh Orchid also occurs in Dorset. It has been reported, but is as yet unconfirmed, from a marshy meadow in west central Dorset, and I have seen colonies which include individual plants which are in some respects intermediate between Southern and Northern Marsh Orchids. There are also several colonies, particularly in the east and southeast of the county, which include a number of individuals intermediate in features between Southern and Narrow-Leaved Marsh Orchids, and which in some cases approach very closely to the most distinct forms of the latter subspecies as it may be found in Oxfordshire, Hampshire, Yorkshire, Anglesey and Ireland. The presence of intermediate plants such as these in Marsh Orchid populations in Dorset makes it important to have some detailed understanding of the distinguishing features of these three subspecies.

Southern Marsh Orchid (*Dactylorhiza majalis* ssp.*praetermissa* (Druce)D. M. Moore & Soó)

Status: fairly common: widespread and locally abundant in Dorset.
Flowering period:

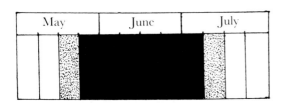

May	June	July

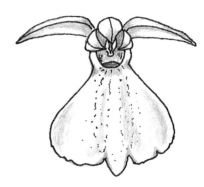

Habitat: most commonly in C, occasional on A & D.

Southern Marsh Orchid *(D.majalis* ssp. *praetermissa)* (×

The Southern Marsh Orchid is often a robust species, ranging in height from 20 to 90cm or even more, with many leaves (usually at least five) and a thick stem. The most frequently encountered form is fairly easily recognised by its concave saucer-shaped lip marked with tiny dots or fine dashes and lines. The lip is occasionally

Map of distribution in Dorset:

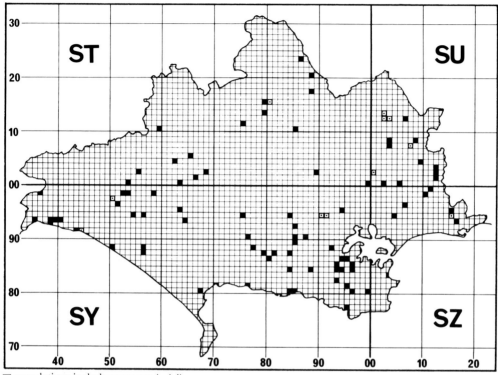

⊡ populations include some var. *junialis*

entire, but is more often three-lobed, with broadly rounded lateral lobes and a smallish tooth-like central lobe. The extent of variation is considerable, although most colonies show a degree of internal homogeneity: some idea of the range of variation normally to be expected in the subspecies is shown on Pages 104 & 109, which shows lip shapes and markings typical of different parts of Dorset. These should not be regarded as exhaustive, however — they are at best only a representative sample. Some forms are so extreme that they have even been afforded varietal status by some authorities, a distinction of debatable value. Some colonies of robust plants near Wimborne St. Giles and on Avon Forest Park for example, in other respects typical of the subspecies, have an unusually lax flower spike and an extremely long central lobe to the lip, and may conceivably be referable to

a rare and enigmatic variety called var. *macrantha*. Spotted-leaved forms occur, although these are very difficult to distinguish from the much more common hybrids with the Spotted Orchids, and may indeed have evolved originally as a result of the stabilisation of hybrid swarms. The so-called 'Leopard' Marsh Orchid is widely regarded as a variety or form of the Southern Marsh Orchid, and should at the present time be correctly classified as ssp. *praetermissa* var. *junialis* (it was formerly known as var. *pardalina*). Current research into this taxon is continuing however, and it may well be reclassified in the near future. It usually has ringed spots, although solid-spotted plants do occur, and has much heavier lip markings in solid deep purple lines and loops. I have however seen hybrids with ring-spotted leaves!

The leaves of the Southern Marsh Orchid

The Tetraploid Marsh Orchids: Lip variations

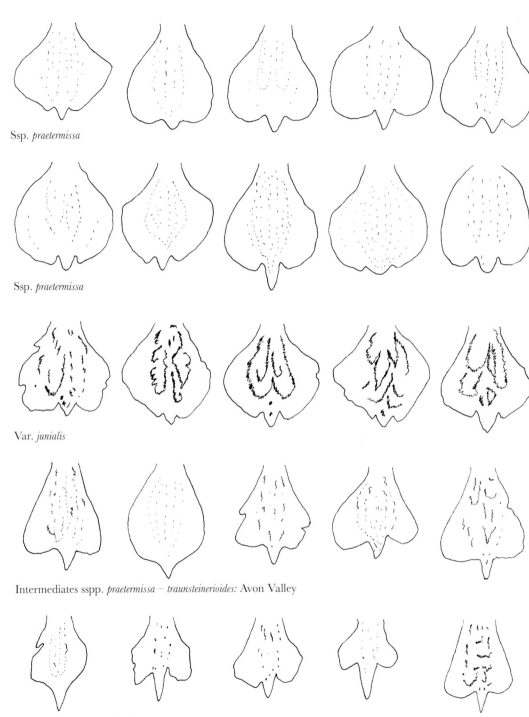

Ssp. *praetermissa*

Ssp. *praetermissa*

Var. *junialis*

Intermediates sspp. *praetermissa – traunsteinerioides:* Avon Valley

Intermediates: Poole Basin

Plate 57: *D.majalis* ssp. *praetermissa*, Avon Forest Park 16.6.86.

Plate 58: Ssp.*praetermissa*, Eype 6.7.85.

in its usual form are generally broad, in excess of 2cm, and may be erect, but are more often spreading, probably by virtue of their weight. Unlike the Early Marsh Orchid, they are rarely keeled and folded, and are only slightly hooded at the tip. They are usually luxuriant, and typically of a rich deep green colour. The floral bracts are usually green, although some brownish-purple anthocyanin staining occurs in some colonies. The flower-spike is long, cylindrical and densely packed with many flowers: in very large plants the spike may be in excess of 20cm in length. In most plants in full flower the floral bracts do not extend markedly beyond the flowers, although they are often more apparent early in the flowering period, before the upper florets are fully open. The spike may also be more conical in shape at that stage. The flowers are generally a lightish rose-red colour, although darker plants do occur, particularly in some western coastal

Plate 59: Ssp.*praetermissa* var. *junialis*, Wimborne St. Giles 20.6.91.

colonies, and some paler plants may fade to a very pale pink late in the flowering period. The lip is usually lightly marked with pale reddish-purple dots and dashes, often concentrated towards the centre of the lip, and which rarely form such clearly-defined loops as the Early Marsh Orchid.

The subspecies can come into flower as early as mid-May, and some plants may last into mid-July, but these extremes are unusual. In an average season in this area, the Southern Marsh Orchid is in good flower in the second and third weeks of June, markedly later than most populations of the Early Marsh Orchid, slightly later than the Narrow-Leaved Marsh Orchid, and a week or two earlier than the Northern Marsh Orchid.

The Southern Marsh Orchid is the most frequently encountered Marsh Orchid in Dorset, being widespread throughout the county, and often locally abundant, although the Leopard Marsh Orchid is less frequently encountered. There are good colonies on the coastal landslips of the Lias and Kimmeridge Clays, where it is often accompanied by the beautiful Marsh Helleborine, and also in the alluvial marshes and wet meadows of the river valleys throughout the county. It is frequent across the marshy heathlands, wet meadows and road verges of the Poole Basin, and even occurs, albeit rarely, on chalk downland, where contrary to some opinion (e.g. Summerhayes 1951) it has persisted for many years, and appears just as at home as in its more customary marshy haunts, although such plants may be rather smaller than most marsh plants.

Northern Marsh Orchid (*Dactylorhiza majalis* ssp. *purpurella* (T. & T. A. Stephenson) D. M. Moore & Soó).

Status: very rare in southern England — formerly two sites in Hampshire, and one doubtful record in Dorset.
Flowering period:

June	July	August
████████████		

Habitat: C only.

Northern Marsh Orchid *(D. majalis* ssp. *purpurella)* (×4)

The Northern Marsh Orchid, also known as the Dwarf Purple Orchid, is the most frequently encountered Marsh Orchid in North Wales, Northern Ireland, northern England and Scotland, its distribution being roughly complementary to that of the

Map of distribution in Dorset:

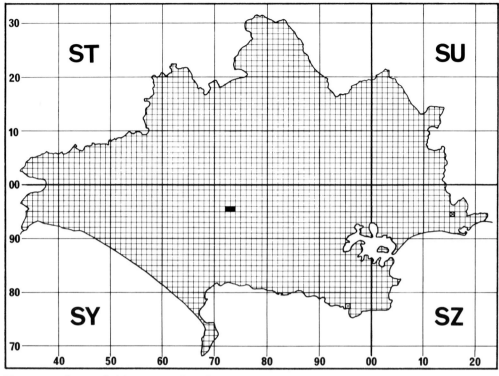

■ ssp.*purpurella* recorded, but not confirmed　　⊡ intermediates sspp.*praetermissa — purpurella*
⊠ hybrid ssp.*praetermissa* × *D.incarnata* (see text)

Southern Marsh Orchid, although there is some overlap in Wales, Lancashire and Yorkshire. The subspecies may now be extinct in the south: it was formerly to be found at two adjacent sites east of Southampton in Hampshire, but as a result of recent drainage, it has declined over the last ten years from a thriving population of several hundred plants to one plant in 1986. The site is now completely dry, and no orchids have been seen there recently. It has been reported from one location near Dorchester, but the plants have not reappeared since 1982, so it has not been possible to confirm the record. At two other sites, one in north Hampshire and one near Minterne Magna in Dorset, where the subspecies has been reported recently, I have been able to check the plants concerned, and

have found rather dark or otherwise rather unusual variations of the Southern Marsh Orchid. It is true to say, however, that there are plants in some southwestern colonies of the Southern Marsh Orchid that are unusually dark in colour, and display some other features of the Northern Marsh Orchid, to the extent that they may be regarded as intermediate between the two subspecies. The intermediate ranges of morphology of all subspecies of the *D.majalis* group are a source of considerable confusion, and require extensive research in Dorset. Hybrids can also cause some confusion: at one site near Christchurch, I recently saw a number of plants that at first sight were typical Northern Marsh Orchid, until closer inspection revealed leaves typical of the Early Marsh Orchid. It then seemed

Plate 60: Ssp.*purpurella*, Southampton, Hants. 26.6.86.

Plate 61: Ssp.*purpurella*, Southampton, Hants. 26.6.86.

likely that these plants were hybrids between the Southern Marsh Orchid and a dark form of the Early Marsh Orchid, both of which occur in abundance at the site.

The Northern Marsh Orchid is generally a smallish plant, ranging in height from 10 to 30cm on average, though occasional robust plants may reach 50cm or more. The stem is noticeably thicker than that of the Narrow-Leaved Marsh Orchid, but rarely reaches the extreme thickness (up to 8-10mm) which is possible in the Southern Marsh Orchid. The leaves (usually five or more) are narrowish, fairly long and spreading, and are often noticeably clustered towards the base of the stem. They are sometimes lightly spotted, particularly towards the leaf-tips, with sparse pinpoint solid spots, and are often slightly hooded at the tip. Floral bracts are usually fairly heavily

stained with anthocyanin. The flower-spike is usually short and blunt, or flat-topped, and densely packed with many flowers. The flowers are generally smaller than those of other members of this group, with a flattish, rather rounded, shallowly three-lobed or diamond-shaped lip, which is usually broadest at or above the middle. The overall colour is the most immediately apparent visual feature: it is generally very dark, ranging from deep bright magenta to deep violet-purple. The lip markings are heavy solid loops, or random lines, spots and dashes in an even deeper colour. The colour difference may be quite startling when it grows with other subspecies, and the vivid colouring of the Northern Marsh Orchid can often be recognised from a considerable distance.

In its northern sites the Northern Marsh

The Tetraploid Marsh Orchids: Lip variations

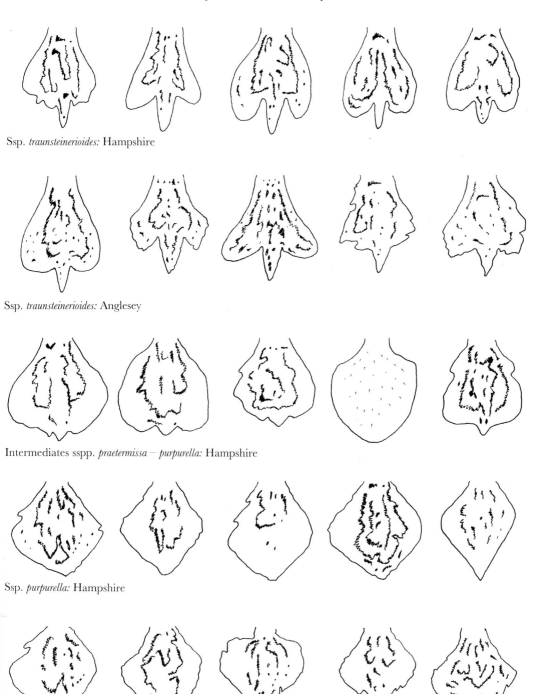

Ssp. *traunsteinerioides:* Hampshire

Ssp. *traunsteinerioides:* Anglesey

Intermediates sspp. *praetermissa – purpurella:* Hampshire

Ssp. *purpurella:* Hampshire

Ssp. *purpurella:* Wales

Orchid can be found in all types of marshland. The Hampshire site, before it was drained, was a dense neutral marsh: the vegetation has thinned progressively in recent years to the stage where it is now no more than a grassy rabbit-grazed field. It once supported an astonishing population of Northern, Southern and Early Marsh Orchids together with both Spotted Orchids, and a startling range of intermediates and hybrids. Its loss is a tragedy for Hampshire. Dorset has much suitable marshland to offer as potential habitat for the Northern Marsh Orchid, and searches for this subspecies may be rewarded.

The subspecies is at its best in July in the north, but this is probably only a latitudinal effect: it flowered from mid-June onwards in Hampshire, a week or so later than the Southern Marsh Orchid, with a considerable overlap in their flowering periods. That feature is not therefore a significant diagnostic factor in the south.

Any information as to possible sightings of the Northern Marsh Orchid in Dorset will always be gratefully received and promptly investigated: research continues into all these difficult Marsh Orchids.

Narrow-Leaved Marsh Orchid (*Dactylorhiza majalis* ssp. *traunsteinerioides* (Pugsley) Bateman & Denholm).

Status: rare — not so far recorded in Dorset in typical form, but a few colonies contain intermediate forms. One population of var. *bowmanii*.

Flowering period:

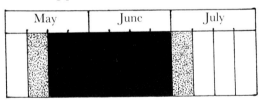

May	June	July

Habitat: C only.

Narrow-Leaved Marsh Orchid
(*D.majalis* ssp. *traunsteinerioides*) (×4)

The Narrow-Leaved Marsh Orchid is a rather rare orchid, most often found in central and western Ireland and in North Wales and Anglesey, although there are isolated colonies in Hampshire, Oxfordshire, East Anglia, Yorkshire and western Scotland. It would appear that the British form of this plant is best assigned to a subspecies of *D.majalis*, although the relationship between it and similar Continental plants known as *D.traunsteineri* (Sauter) Soó, to which British plants had been assigned until recently, is not yet clear, and is the subject of current research. Early indications are that they are not distinct, and European plants should also therefore be treated as belonging to a subspecies of *D.majalis* (as ssp. *traunsteineri* (Sauter) Sundermann).

There are two widely separated colonies in Hampshire which contain a number of plants which approach very closely to the typical subspecies, and several colonies in Dorset containing a number of plants intermediate in morphology between the Southern and Narrow-Leaved Marsh Orchids. A newly identified form,

Map of distribution in Dorset:

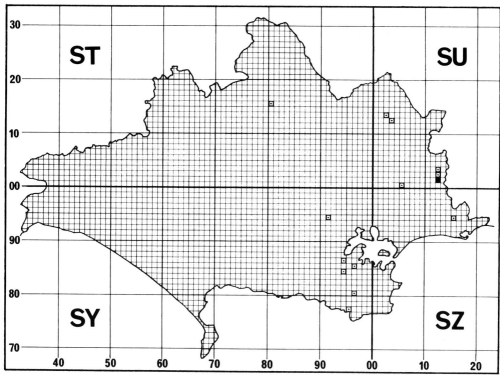

⊡ intermediates sspp.*praetermissa — traunsteinerioides*   ■ ssp.*traunsteinerioides* var.*bowmanii*

var.*bowmanii* Jenkinson, more robust than the type (see Plates 62 & 63) occurs at two sites, one at Exbury in Hampshire, and one in Dorset (Avon Forest Park), although at this stage it appears that the typical subspecies does not occur in Dorset. Much research in this area is still needed however: the Hampshire colony was only discovered as recently as 1985, and the Dorset site was identified only three years ago (1988).

The Narrow-Leaved Marsh Orchid is typically a small, thin-stemmed plant, ranging in height from 10 to 30cm, with few leaves (not usually more than four), which are markedly narrower than those of any other Marsh Orchid. They are almost always less than 2cm in width, and usually much less (around 1 to 1.5cm), and are also often folded inwards along the keel and twisted, thus appearing even narrower. They

are usually erect, and do not normally extend beyond the flowers. The flower-spike is short and lax, with few flowers, and is often one-sided. The floral bracts are invariably anthocyanin-stained to some degree, often intensely so. The leaves are sometimes lightly spotted, particularly towards the leaf-tips, with pinpoint or transversely elongated solid spots. Leaf-spotting is rare, however, in southern colonies. The flowers are usually comparatively large by Marsh Orchid standards, with a lip that is widest towards the bottom, with well-rounded and markedly reflexed lateral lobes. The central lobe is almost invariably long and pointed, usually extending well beyond the laterals. The flower colour is similar to that of the Southern Marsh Orchid, or a shade or two deeper and brighter, and the lip markings are generally smudged dots and dashes in

Plate 62: Ssp.*traunsteinerioides* var. *bowmanii*,
Exbury, Hants. 19.6.86.

firmly in another. It is the total sum of features which is important: juvenile, stunted or genetically defective plants in colonies of the Southern Marsh Orchid may show dwarfing or abnormally narrow leaves, or late in the flowering period may present lips with reflexed lateral lobes. Likewise some colonies in very alkaline marshes may show exceptionally deep purple staining of the bracts. A degree of homogeneity in a colony is indicative of one subspecies, whereas a clear bimodality of form within a colony may be an indication of the presence of two subspecies. The colonies in Dorset, containing intermediate plants referred to above, are of immense importance to current research into this enigmatic taxon: the very presence of intermediates goes a long way to support the contention that these plants should be regarded as a subspecies of the *D.majalis* group.

vague concentric loops covering most of the lip surface. They may be of a quite intense colour — Anglesey and Yorkshire colonies tend to be rather darker.

Var.*bowmanii* has slightly broader and longer leaves than the type and occasionally has five leaves, but its most distinctive feature is the comparatively narrow extremely deeply three-lobed lip. The flower colour is also rather dark, similar to some Yorkshire colonies, and is most noticeable in mixed colonies with ssp.*praetermissa*.

Many colonies of the Southern Marsh Orchid will be found to contain a few plants with one or two features of the Narrow-Leaved Marsh Orchid, in particular the extension of the central lobe or the type of lip markings, or the overall size of the plants and the number and narrowness of the leaves. Individual features appearing in this way are not sufficient justification for assigning individual plants to one subspecies, when the overall sum of the features of the majority of plants in a colony places them

Plate 63: Var.*bowmanii*, Exbury, Hants. 19.6.86.

Typically a fen plant in most of its stations, the Narrow-Leaved Marsh Orchid often grows in standing water amongst reeds. It may also be found, however, in other types of marshland or wet meadow, although such sites will usually be found to be quite strongly calcareous. It is particularly characteristic of basic flushes in Yorkshire and Scotland. Var. *bowmanii* however extends the species' habitat range quite markedly as at the Dorset site in particular it grows in relatively dry acid grassland. It flowers normally a week or two earlier than the Southern Marsh Orchid, coming into flower first in late May, and lasting until mid-June, although the extremely wide flowering range of the commoner subspecies makes overlap frequent. The flowering period of var.*bowmanii* is roughly contemporaneous with ssp.*praetermissa*, at its peak in early to mid-June.

References and Bibliography

Angel, H. *et al* (1981): The Natural History of Britain and Ireland (George Rainbird Ltd., and Book Club Associates, London).

Bateman, R. M. (1979): *Epipactis purpurata* —Violet Helleborine (J. Orchid Soc. Gr. Br., 28).

Bateman, R. M. (1981): The Hertfordshire *Orchidaceae* (Trans. Herts. Nat. Hist. Fld. Club, 28).

Bateman, R. M. & Denholm, I. (1983, 1985 & 1989b): A reappraisal of the British and Irish dactylorchids,

1. The tetraploid marsh-orchids (Watsonia,[1] Vol.14),

2. The diploid marsh-orchids (Watsonia, Vol.15), and

3. The spotted-orchids (Watsonia, Vol.17).

Bateman, R. M. & Denholm, I. (1989a): Morphometric procedure, taxonomic objectivity and marsh-orchid systematics (Watsonia, Vol.17).

Blamey, M., Fitter, R. & A. (1978): The Wild Flowers of Britain and Northern Europe (Collins, London).

Bulow-Olsen, A. (1978): Plant Communities (Penguin, London).

Clapham, A. R., Tutin, T. G. & Warburg, E. F. (1962): Flora of the British Isles (2nd edition)(Cambridge University Press).

Courtney, E. M., Curtis, L. F. & Trudgill, S. (1976): Soils in the British Isles (Longman, London).

Davies, P. & J., & Huxley, A. (1983): Wild Orchids of Britain and Europe (Chatto & Windus, London).

Dorset Trust for Nature Conservation (1980 *et seq.*): Guide to Reserves (DTNC, Bournemouth).

Ettlinger, D. M. T. (1976): British and Irish Orchids, a Field Guide (MacMillan, London).

Fitter, R. S. R. & McLintock, D. (1973): Collins Pocket Guide to Wild Flowers (Collins, London).

Godfery, M. J. (1933): Monograph and Iconograph of Native British Orchidaceae (Cambridge).

Good, R. (1948): A Geographical Handbook of the Dorset Flora (DNH & AS, Dorchester).

Good, R. (1984): A Concise Flora of Dorset (DNH & AS, Dorchester).

Grierson, M. & Hunt, P. F. (1978): The Country Life Book of Orchids (Country Life Books, London).

Hampshire County Council (various authors)(1983-4): Hampshire Countryside Heritage Booklets, (2) Ancient Woodland, (3) Rivers and Wetlands, (4) Heathland, (6) Chalk Grassland, and

(9) Meadows (HCC with Nature Conservancy Council, Winchester).

HMSO (1960): British Regional Geology: The Hampshire Basin and Adjoining Areas (3rd edition, London).

Hywel-Davies, J. & Thom, V. (1984): The MacMillan Guide to Britain's Nature Reserves (MacMillan, London).

Jenkinson, M. N. (1986): The Narrow-Leaved Marsh Orchid in Hampshire: a threatened site (report to the Nature Conservancy Council —unpublished).

Jenkinson, M. N. (1986): A Comparison of Marsh Orchids in North Wales and Southern

England (report to the Nature Conservation bodies of Wales — unpublished).

Jenkinson, M. N. (1992): The Marsh Orchids in Hampshire and Dorset: Recent Research. (Proc. Hants. Fld. Club & Arch. Soc., Vol.47 — in press).

Jenkinson, M. N. & Hobson, A. G. (1989): *Epipactis purpurata* Sm. reappears in Dorset (Watsonia, Vol.17).

King, M. P. (1974): Beneath Your Feet: The Geology and Scenery of Bournemouth (Purbeck Press).

Linton, E. F. (1900): Flora of Bournemouth.

Mansell-Pleydell, J. C. (1874 & 1895): The Flora of Dorsetshire (Dorchester).

Martin, W. K. (1975): The Concise British Flora in Colour (Book Club Associates, London).

Moore, P. D. (1980): The Mitchell Beazley Pocket Guide to Wild Flowers (Mitchell Beazley, London).

Phillips, R. (1980): Wild Flowers of Britain (Pan Books, London).

Reinhard, H. R. (1985): Skandinavische und Alpine Dactylorhiza-Arten (*Orchidaceae*)(AHO, Baden-Württemberg).

Roberts, R. H. (1961a & b, 1966): Studies on Welsh Orchids,

1. The Variation of *Dactylorchis purpurella* (T & T. A. Steph.)Vermeul. in North Wales (Watsonia, Vol.5),

2. The Occurrence of *Dactylorchis majalis* (Reichb.)Vermeul. in Wales (Watsonia, Vol.5), and

3. The Coexistence of Some of the Tetraploid Species of Marsh Orchids (Watsonia, Vol.6).

Roberts, R. H. (1988): The occurrence of *Dactylorhiza traunsteineri* (Sauter)Soó in Britain and Ireland (Watsonia, Vol.17).

Roberts, S. (1984): Wild Flowers of Dorset (Dovecote Press, Wimborne).

Sanford, M. N. (1991): The Orchids of Suffolk (Suffolk Naturalists Society).

Senghas, K. & Sundermann, H. (1968): Probleme der Orchideengattung *Dactylorhiza* (Wuppertal).

Smith, A. E. (Ed.) (1982): A Nature Reserves Handbook (RSNC, Lincoln).

Summerhayes, V. S. (1951, & 2nd edit. 1968): Wild Orchids of Britain (Collins, London).

Turrill, W. B. (1962): British Plant Life (Collins, London).

Tutin, T. G. (Ed.) (1980): *Flora Europaea* Vol.V (Cambridge University Press).

Vermeulen, P. (1947): Studies on Dactylorchids (Utrecht).

Young, D. P. (1952 & 1962): Studies in the British *Epipactis*,

III. *Epipactis phyllanthes* G. E. Sm., an overlooked species (Watsonia, Vol.2),

V. *Epipactis leptochila*: et al., and

VI. Some further notes on *E.phyllanthes* (Watsonia Vol.5).

[1]'Watsonia' is the journal of the Botanical Society of the British Isles.

Index to Species

(Figures in italics indicate brief references, figures in roman type indicate the detailed section on the species, and figures in brackets indicate the colour plate numbers.)